Behavioral Individuality in Early Childhood

Behavioral Individuality

in Early Childhood

ALEXANDER THOMAS, M.D.
Associate Professor, Psychiatry
New York University School of Medicine

STELLA CHESS, M.D.
Associate Professor, Psychiatry
New York Medical College

HERBERT G. BIRCH, M.D., PH.D.
Associate Research Professor, Pediatrics
Albert Einstein College of Medicine

MARGARET E. HERTZIG, M.D.
Resident in Psychiatry
Bellevue Hospital

SAM KORN, PH.D.
Assistant Professor, Psychology
Hunter College

NEW YORK UNIVERSITY PRESS

Third Printing 1971

ISBN-0-8147-0414-X

© 1963 BY NEW YORK UNIVERSITY
LIBRARY OF CONGRESS CATALOG CARD NUMBER: 63-18666
MANUFACTURED IN THE UNITED STATES OF AMERICA

PREFACE

THE STUDY of which the results reported in the present volume are a part began with a concern over the apparent one-sidedness of the prevalent approach to the development of personality. On clinical grounds it has long been evident that no consistent and direct relation can be found between parental practices and attitudes and other environmental influences and the specific nature of personality organization in a given child. Inevitably such findings raise the question of the contribution of the child's own characteristics of reactivity to the child-environment interaction and suggest that the direction of development might be considerably influenced by the nature of the child as an organism. Despite these considerations, contemporary style, both in theories of child personality and in clinical practice in child psychiatry, has been dominated by an environmentalist view. The problems and behaviors of children have been almost exclusively considered as deriving from patterns of intra- and extrafamilial influence. Little systematic attention has been paid to the child's own contribution to his development. Therefore, in 1952 we began to explore the relation of the child's reaction patterning to his personality development. This exploration developed in 1956 into a systematic longitudinal study which has been in progress since that date.

It is easy for any emphasis in investigation to achieve exclusiveness. This danger in our study could lead to a one-sidedness based upon organismic characteristics which would be at least as pronounced as that reflected in the more prevalent environmentalist viewpoint. Such a position is antithetical to us because of our primary attachment to an interactionist theory. Our concern, therefore, is not with the organismic determination of personality, but rather with the interplay of organismic and environmental forces in the development of the child.

Two paths are open to the investigator who wishes to explore

v

the development of such an interaction. The first involves the attempt at a global estimation of functional relationships in development. We have avoided this approach because of the conviction that it has intrinsic properties which result in diffuseness and limit consideration to qualitative description. The second approach involves an initial process of dissection in which organismic and environmental factors are each at first independently considered. The independent explorations may then be integrated and their interdependencies determined. It is this second path which has been followed in our study. Therefore, when we direct attention exclusively to organismic characteristics, we do so not because we believe that they alone are responsible for personality development, but rather because exclusive concentration on an aspect of development is essential if we are to learn its laws.

The study of development during the first two years of life reported in the present volume has occurred against these background considerations. It is a longitudinal study, and as such has made considerable demands upon the children and their parents. The oldest of the 130 children studied from the first months of life are now in their eighth year. To have maintained a sample stability of greater than 95 percent over so long a period is a tribute to the cooperativeness and devotion to knowledge of the parents. We take this opportunity to express our gratitude to them for having made this study possible. In addition, the opportunity for studying the children in nursery school and in the first school years was possible only because of the wholehearted cooperation of the schools and the teachers.

Our debt to our research assistants, interviewers, and colleagues is large. In particular, we would like to take this opportunity to thank Sophie Ladimer, Sylvia Zuckerman, Martha Roth, Rae Thomas, Mimi Korn, Celia Kreiss, and Ida Hafner for their continuing contributions.

Long-term behavioral studies are expensive, and one of the scope of our own could not have proceeded without financial support. At the beginning private sources, including The Gralnick Foundation, were generous in the provision of funds. Over the years of most intensive work support derived in large part from the National Institute of Mental Health (Research Grants M–2805 [A] and M–3614).

The Authors

CONTENTS

THE RESEARCH PROGRAM of which this monograph represents a part started out with the basic conviction that temperamental characteristics of the infant make a fundamental contribution to the development of psychological individuality. It is our view that personality development is the result of the interaction of a baby endowed with definable characteristics of initial reactivity and an environmental complex including familial and extrafamilial factors. The data available for exploring the process of interaction have been insufficient because most investigations in both developmental psychology and child psychiatry have tended to focus one-sidedly upon the environmental contributions to development. The role of organismic characteristics in psychological development has received some attention in terms of the view that developmental level is a fundamental factor in structuring the child's reactions to his environment. However, the concept of developmental level has in the main referred to general laws of responsiveness and to the time sequence in which universals in personality organization have been achieved, but not to the problem of individuality or uniqueness of functioning.

Especially in the United States [1,2] the primary emphasis has been placed upon the environmental or experiential determination of individuality. The tendency to seek the source of individuality in environmental influences on the developing child is not limited to any one school of thought. It has been manifest both in those inquiries basing themselves on psychoanalytic conceptualization and in those deriving from more traditional positions in academic psychology. The differences between these approaches have been reflected in the aspects of the environment that each school has selected as being most influential in determining the course of development, and not in a disagreement as to the fundamental and often exclusive acceptance of environmental determinance. The psychoanalytic movement has been dominated in its selection by the view that prime importance in the child's develop-ment must be assigned to intrafamilial phenomena manifested during the first years of life. Thus such workers as Levy,[3] Ribble,[4] Hartman,[5] Sullivan,[6] Anna Freud,[7] and Bowlby,[8] have focused on early mother-child interactions and later sibling relations as the critical factors in determining individual styles of development. Others of a general psy-choanalytic school, such as Kardiner,[9] Horney,[10] Erikson,[11] Fromm,[12] and Murphy,[13] have added to the intrafamilial components a group of influential factors related to certain broader aspects of social and cultural experience. The traditional psychology has directed its atten-tion either to minutiae of response, such as reaction time and sensory threshold, or, in its sociological segment, to the influence on develop-ment exerted by such broad social phenomena as class and ethnic characteristics.[14,15]

In both approaches, until quite recently, little or no systematic attention has been focused upon the initial biologic characteristics of infants as significant factors in determining the development of psy-chological individuality. Over the last few years, however, a number of studies have reported observations on individual differences in the infant and young child in specific discrete areas such as sensory thresh-old,[16] motility,[17] perceptual responses,[18] sleeping and feeding pat-terns,[19] drive endowment,[20] quality and intensity of emotional tone,[21] social responsiveness,[22] autonomic response patterns,[23,24] biochemical individuality,[25] and electroencephalographic patterns.[26] These various reports have emphasized that certain individual differences potentially important for behavioral functioning appear to be present at birth or shortly thereafter and are not the result of postnatal experience.

Despite their limited character, the findings of these studies were in accord with the view that important individual differences in re-sponsiveness did exist in young infants. However, the pertinence of these characteristics for later development was unknown. What ap-peared to be necessary was detailed longitudinal information on the relation of early reactivity to later functioning. To solve this problem, it was necessary to undertake the following:

1] The development of a method for classifying the individuality of behavioral responsiveness of young infants in terms of objectively describable and reliably rated categories of reactivity.

2] The study of the persistence of these initial characteristics in the course of development.

3] The analysis of the pertinence of the child's characteristics of initial reactivity to his later individuality in adaptive organization.

4] The exploration of the relation of initial reactivity to the development of temperament.

5] The analysis of the relevance of initial responsivity to the possible development of later behavior aberrations.

6] The study of the degree to which characteristics of initial reactivity may serve to determine parental reactions to the child.

7] The analysis of the interaction of parental attitudes and practices with initial reactivity as a significant determinative process in personality development.

In the present monograph we have limited ourselves to the events of the first two years of life. Accordingly, we shall report the manner in which we have been able to identify initial characteristics of reactivity, the methods for the rating of such characteristics, the persistence and variability of these characteristics through the first two years, and the relation of initial reactivity to adaptive course and to parent-child relations during this defined period.

REFERENCES

1. G. W. Allport, "European and American Theories of Personality," *Perspectives in Personality Theory*, eds. H. P. David and H. von Bracken (New York: Basic Books, 1961), pp. 3–24.

2. A. M. Rose, ed., *Mental Health and Mental Disorder* (New York: W. W. Norton & Co., Inc., 1955).

3. D. Levy, *Maternal Overprotection* (New York: Columbia University Press, 1943).

4. M. Ribble, *The Rights of Infants* (New York: Columbia University Press, 1943).

5. H. Hartman, "Psychoanalysis and Developmental Psychology," *Psychoanalytic Study of the Child*, 5:12 (1950).

6. H. S. Sullivan, *The Interpersonal Theory of Psychiatry* (New York: W. W. Norton & Co., Inc., 1953).

7. A. Freud, *The Ego and the Mechanisms of Defense* (London: The Hogarth Press Ltd., 1948).

8. J. Bowlby, "Maternal Care and Mental Health," World Health Organization, Monograph No. 3 (Geneva, 1951).

9. A. Kardiner, *The Psychological Frontiers of Society* (New York: Columbia University Press, 1945).

10. K. Horney, *The Neurotic Personality of Our Time* (New York: W. W. Norton & Co., Inc., 1937).

11. E. H. Erikson, *Childhood and Society* (New York: W. W. Norton & Co., Inc., 1950).

12. E. Fromm, *Man for Himself* (New York: Rinehart & Co., 1947).

13. G. Murphy, *A Biosocial Approach to Origins and Structure* (New York: Harper and Bros., 1947).

14. A. Anastasi and J. P. Foley, Jr., *Differential Psychology* (New York: Macmillan Co., 1949).

15. L. Tyler, *The Psychology of Human Differences* (New York: Appleton-Century-Crofts, 1956).

16. P. Bergman and S. Escalona, "Unusual Sensitivities in Very Young Children," *Psychoanalytic Study of the Child*, 3–4:333 (1949).

17. M. Fries and P. Woolf, "Some Hypotheses on the Role of the Congenital Activity Type in Development," *Psychoanalytic Study of the Child*, 8:48 (1953).

18. H. A. Witkin and Others, *Psychological Differentiation* (New York: John Wiley & Sons, 1962).

19. S. Escalona, "Emotional Development in the First Year of Life," *Problems of Infancy and Childhood* (New York: Josiah Macy, Jr. Foundation, 1953), p. 11.

20. A. Alpert, P. W. Neubauer, and A. P. Weil, "Unusual Variation in Drive Endowment," *Psychoanalytic Study of the Child*, 11:125 (1956).

21. R. Meili, "A Longitudinal Study of Personality Development," *Dynamic Psychopathology in Childhood*, eds. L. Jessner and E. Pavenstedt (New York: Grune & Stratton, 1959), pp. 106–123. [This is a summary of a monographic report, "Anfange der Charakterentwicklung" (Bern: Hans Hunber, 1957.)]

22. A. Gesell and L. B. Ames, "Early Evidences of Individuality in the Human Infant," *Journal of Genetic Psychology*, 47:339 (1937).

23. W. H. Bridger and M. F. Reiser, "Psychophysiologic Studies of the Neonate," *Psychosomatic Medicine*, 21:265 (1959).

24. E. L. Lipton, A. Steinschneider, and J. B. Richmond, "Autonomic Function in the Neonate," *Psychosomatic Medicine*, 23:472 (1961).

25. R. V. Williams, *Biochemical Individuality* (New York: John Wiley & Sons, 1956).

26. G. Walter, "Electroencephalographic Development of Children," *Discussions on Child Development*, eds. J. M. Tanner and B. Inhelder (New York: International Universities Press, 1953), I, 132–160.

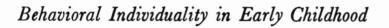

Behavioral Individuality in Early Childhood

I

General Considerations

THE PRESENT INVESTIGATION is concerned with identifying characteristics of individuality in behavior during the first months of life and with exploring the degree to which these characteristics are persistent and influence the development of later psychological organization. This inquiry is being carried out through the longitudinal study of a group of 130 children from the first months of life onward. Although the study proper is now in its eighth year, the present report concerns itself only with the first two years of life. Consequently, the main issues dealt with here are: 1] the manner in which initial patterning of behavioral functioning may be identified; 2] the methodologic problems of behavioral characterization; and 3] the stability of initial patterns of reactivity through the first two years of life. Subsequent publications will extend the reporting into the preschool and early school years.

To avoid fruitless polemic, it is important from the outset to distinguish between the terms "significant" determinant and "sole" determinant. It is obvious to all students of behavior that factors other than initial reactivity affect developmental course. Therefore, the present study in no way denies the existence of social, environmental, or interpersonal influences upon psychological development. However, in any multidetermined system it is entirely appropriate to select one of the variables for detailed scrutiny and to determine the significance of its contribution to the phenomena under consideration. Such selectivity, of course, requires the control of other potentially influential variables so that the results obtained can in fact be related to the hypothesis and are not the artifactual products of other uncontrolled influences. Operationally, therefore, our problem is that of determining the contribution to the developmental process that is made by the patterns of reactivity observable in the child during early infancy.

The development of predictive indices and the identification of characteristics which may be sequentially explored during growth may be pursued in either of two ways: the hypothetico-deductive or the inductive. The first alternative would involve the a priori statement of the characteristics of early reactivity that were of significance to later individuality in psychological development. Such a statement would necessarily be based upon a theoretical scheme which delineated the relationship and pertinence of specifiable aspects of early reactivity through the analysis of the actual observable characteristics of behavior in the young child. It is our conviction that no fully adequate theoretic scheme is available, and that at this stage an inductive hypothesis-producing rather than a deductive hypothesis-testing course is to be preferred.

We have thus committed ourselves to the task of analyzing behavior, longitudinally sampled, with the aim of teasing out developmental relationships.

To obtain detailed longitudinal data on a sufficiently large sample of children for specifying a variety of patterns of initial reactivity, it was necessary to secure a readily available and investigatively economical source of data. The direct continuous observation of the child would require a ratio of one investigator to each child. Consequently, the choice of the direct observational method has in other investigations led to episodic study in place of sustained inquiry. It appeared to us that the data-gathering problem would be solved if it were recognized that the parent represented a potential source of continual direct observation, and that parental experience, if adequately assessed, constituted a basic and economical source of information on development. The following questions arise in the use of the parent as a source of data: 1] Can the parent supply sufficient explicit behavioral in-

formation for analysis? 2] Is this information adequate for studying the problem at issue? 3] Are the observations valid reflections
of the child's actual functioning? If these questions can be answered in the affirmative, then information on a large sample of
children can be obtained which could otherwise be gathered only
by a large corps of investigators living in the homes of the subjects.
The manner in which these methodologic questions were answered
will be dealt with in Chapter V.

Since we clearly recognized that sociocultural factors constituted another effective variable in determining the course of
psychological development, we believed that the contribution of
initial reactivity to the developmental process could best be seen
if sociocultural variability were minimized. Consequently, we
chose for our study a group which is relatively homogeneous from
a sociocultural and economic point of view. In a heterogeneous
group it would be difficult to decide whether observed individual
differences in behavior were extensions of differences in initial
reactivity or were caused by differences in social background and
economic standing, by special social stresses, by varying approaches
to child care practices, and so on. The use of a homogeneous group
does not, of course, eliminate all of the differences in environment
which impinge upon the infant. There are still variations in attitudes, psychological patterns within the family, and developmental
experiences which will affect the child. However, the relative
homogeneity of the group does serve to minimize the influence of
gross cultural and economic factors, so that the individual differences observed are more likely to reflect the role of initial differences as they interact with individual parental attitudes and practices and with such special environmental factors as the birth of a
sibling, illness, or unusual stresses in the home.

Clearly, the specific set of characteristics selected for the
definition of individuality depends on the object of the inquiry.
If a study is concerned with the effects of different food intakes,
then individual heights and weights will probably be important.
If intellectual functioning is examined, the characteristics selected
for study may involve variations in performance in a standard
I.Q. test. Similarly, an investigation concerned with anthropologi-

cal questions will consider ethnic characteristics. It is meaningless to argue in the abstract whether one definition of individuality is superior to another. The important question is: What goal does each definition of individual difference permit one to achieve? The present investigation is concerned with the study of individuality in initial behavioral organization and its significance, if any, for later psychological functioning. Our goal, therefore, is to identify one set of formal behavioral characteristics which will permit the categorization of the broadest possible spectrum of everyday behavior. We are interested in delineating the minimum number of significant categories of function which may be identified as accounting for the range of individual behavioral differences.

In our study we have focused as sharply and at the same time as broadly as possible on the characteristics of individual behavioral differences found among infants during the first three months of life. By tracing the fate of these attributes—which we have called initial characteristics of reactivity *—we have sought to determine which of the initial patterns of functioning proved to be persistent as the infants grew older and to explore the ways in which they were significant in influencing later behavioral development. In order to define the nature of early individuality in behavior, we have utilized the data derived from a longitudinal, anterospective study of activities in daily life in the early infancy period. We have then related these behaviors to later developing functions.

The question may be raised as to the special value of anterospective investigation, since retrospective studies have been a primary source of data in both psychology and psychiatry. We do not believe that retrospective analysis can be used satisfactorily to uncover early individual characteristics. In order to make events in the past correspond to current phenomena, attitude dis-

---

* Objection may be taken to calling such behaviors initial. Other workers may wish to reserve this term for immediate postnatal reactivity or even for such phenomena as prenatal intrauterine activity levels in gross motor and autonomic functions. Such reservation may very well be legitimate, but from an operational point of view it is entirely appropriate to designate the functioning of the infant during the first three months of life as his initial behavioral characterization.

tortions affecting memory necessarily occur. Freud himself was aware of this possibility when he said, "So long as we trace the development [of a mental process] backwards, the connection appears continuous, and we feel we have gained an insight which is completely satisfactory and even exhaustive. But if we proceed the reverse way, if we start from the premise inferred from the analysis and try to follow up to the final result, then we no longer get the impression of an inevitable sequence of events, which could not have been otherwise determined. We notice at once that there might be another result, and that we might have been just as well able to understand and explain the latter." [1] Additional inaccuracies may stem from emotional attitudes and special biases of the reporter.[2] The present relationship of parent to child and of child to parent will obviously influence the recollection of events. Cultural attitudes, too, may create distortions of retrospective recall. A parent whose sociocultural group stresses cleanliness or intellectual ability is likely to describe behavior considered desirable by peers rather than the child's actual toilet training or reactions to learning situations. Therefore, interviews with older children or adults concerning their infancy can seldom be accepted as accurate recall of events or processes. In our study when we asked parents to recall important details of their children's functioning after a two-year interval, we found significant distortions of accuracy. As an instance, 28 percent of the mothers whose children had sucked their thumbs stated that this had never happened.[3]

Freud found that the reports of his patients describing experiences of sexual seduction in early childhood were based on fantasy instead of fact. While he could still use these distortions effectively for psychoanalytic clinical purposes, they were of little value in systematic ontogenetic study. Even when some of the information obtained through retrospective interviews is accurate, it provides only a partial basis for reconstructing the sequences and determinative forces involved in the psychological evolution of an individual. These considerations make it necessary that the study of the ontogenesis of individuality in functioning be pursued anterospectively, and that the data derived from parental interview be obtained frequently enough to guarantee the minimization of temporal distorting effects on recall.

A second requirement in an effective longitudinal study is the identification of the characteristics to be followed. In the present study such characteristics have been induced from content analysis of parental interview protocols. By this means we have sought to delineate behavioral characteristics which are ubiquitously present in the children and which represent the continua along which they vary. Each infant has been characterized by his scale position on each of these characteristics.

The ultimate goal of the analysis has been the identification of variables and categories in terms of formal characteristics rather than of contents of individual behavior. The distinction between the content and the formal characteristics of behavior is crucial in the longitudinal study of behavioral stability. It is a truism that content is continuously changing and therefore necessarily unstable as an index of the persistence of individual attributes of function. In contrast, formal characteristics of behavior may be constant within a framework of changing content. Thus distractibility as a formal characteristic may be expressed in terms of the ease with which bottle feeding is interfered with by external stimulation at age six months, and in the ready disturbance of ongoing academic work by extraneous noise in the school years. In each case the formal aspect is the same, although the content of behavior is markedly different. In the present study attention is directed to the formal aspects of behavior and not to the content.

Formal characteristics may be defined as those present in a variety of behaviors irrespective of content. In general, all scientific investigation is similarly concerned with the definition and study of formal characteristics. Physics is concerned with velocity, force, volume, mass. Chemistry deals with valences, biology with irritability. In each discipline the scientist abstracts from the specific content those particular formal characteristics which are of interest and importance to his investigation. His aim is to analyze these characteristics in common terms, irrespective of the diverse and separate contexts in which they occur. Force, for instance, can be studied in the abstract and a general formula arrived at which will be equally applicable to the specific conditions of a gas, coal, or electric engine. In a similar way we have sought to analyze the initial formal characteristics of behavior which can be abstracted from the many diverse contents in which they occur. An infant sleeps, eats, plays, responds to outside stimuli. These are contents of behavior. The formal characteristics underlying them may be described in terms of activity level, intensity of reaction, adaptability, and so forth. Our concern is with the manner in which these initially present formal characteristics are patterned in the individual and with their influence on the developmental process.

REFERENCES

1. S. Freud, *Collected Papers* (London: The Hogarth Press Ltd., 1950), II, 226.
2. K. E. Goddard, G. Broder, and C. Wenar, "Reliability of Pediatric Histories: A Preliminary Study," *Pediatrics,* 28:1011 (1961).
3. L. Robbins, "The Accuracy of Parental Recall of Aspects of Child Development and of Child-Rearing Practices," *Journal of Abnormal and Social Psychology,* 66:261 (1963).

II

Issues in Longitudinal Studies

ALTHOUGH MANY ASPECTS of growth and development may be adequately investigated by means of successive matched age stage samples, longitudinal study is uniquely effective in the exploration of: r] the relation between earlier characteristics of the individual and features of later development (developmental process or prognosis); and 2] the delineation of individual behavioral sequences. For most other questions serial sampling of appropriate populations at different ages represents an entirely adequate and more efficient study design. For example, a knowledge of the ossification centers or the behavioral skills characteristic of children at different ages can be determined by the simultaneous study of representative samples drawn from different age groups. If, however, one is concerned with such developmental questions as whether the presence of a given ossification center is pathognomonic or whether the I.Q.'s of children are constant, one is forced to study the same individual at more than one point in time, that is, to pursue a longitudinal investigation.

It can be stated, as Kodlin and Thompson have, that: "r] the longitudinal approach is the only approach which gives a complete description of the growth phenomenon, and 2] the cross-sectional approach can never satisfy the objective of a study which requires the measurement of the change in a trait through time in a given individual." [1] This means that when the object of the growth study is to arrive at predictions of individual growth generally, or to establish the correlations between measurements obtained at successive ages, it is necessary to employ the longitudinal approach.

All longitudinal studies of growth which seek to study the relationship between such physical attributes as height, weight, head circumference, ossification centers, and dentition at different ages, have a common design. A representative population sample is selected and the particular physical characteristic under consideration is studied at appropriate intervals. Initial information is objectively obtained and readily verified. Subsequent investigation is a replication of the initial data-gathering procedure, as correlations are sought between variables which are qualitatively identifiable at all stages of development. This basic design, which involves the selection of initial variables, the following of these variables in time, and the making of correlations between variables at successive ages, must underlie the longitudinal study of personality development as well. However, longitudinal studies of psychological characteristics cannot be approached with the same degree of facility because: *1*] there is no general agreement as to the characteristics which have psychological importance at any stage of development; *2*] psychological functions in development change qualitatively in relation to time and the characteristics initially studied may no longer be present at a later age stage; *3*] the relation between earlier and later attributes of psychological functioning, and thus the pertinence of the initial characteristics measured to later outcome, is not immediately apparent; and *4*] the selection of methods for the reliable and valid assessment of psychological characteristics, and the measurement of the traits to be interrelated pose a considerable problem requiring the development of objective techniques.

In view of the logic of the longitudinal method and the kinds of problems to which it is pertinent, it is clear that, when psychological characteristics are considered, the method is principally applicable to the study of age stage characteristics of an individual's functioning. Further, if the method is to be effectively employed, one must, as in the case of the longitudinal studies of physical growth, identify objectively measurable characteristics of individual functioning which may either themselves or through their sequelae be followed in time. These considerations provide the fundamental prerequisities for pursuing any longitudinal study of psychological development.

A failure to meet some or all of these requirements becomes apparent when one reviews the longitudinal investigations of personality development collected by Stone and Onqué [2] in their annotated bibliography. Many of these studies were initiated without a clear conception of the features of psychological development which it was either desirable or possible to measure. Moreover, subsequent psychological inquiry, whether conducted by means of testing, observations of children, or interviews with parents, was often undertaken at different times and with different groups of children, so that no truly comparable longitudinal data were forthcoming. The general confusion produced by these attempts has been succinctly described by Escalona, who has remarked that "in the absence of specific questions to be asked of the data all kinds of information that could be obtained about the subjects of the study have at times been unselectively accumulated. When the data were subsequently analyzed and reported, much of the available information held but little interest to the investigation, with files upon files of developmental data still gathering dust in many places. More frustrating yet, it has been a common experience that after a number of years, investigators found that they lacked the very facts which they would currently find of greatest interest but played no significant part in their thinking when the longitudinal study was begun." [3] To this criticism one may add that in many studies changes in methods of data collection occurred from year to year in accordance with the dictates of current psychological fashion.

Both a desire to determine general stages of personality development and an interest in developmental individuality have motivated recent investigations. From what has already been said only the latter of these interests requires the longitudinal method, since the uncovering of general normative stages of development can be pursued more economically and effectively by cross-sectional study.

From their inception all longitudinal studies of personality development have encountered difficulties in: *1*] the definition of initially important attributes of personality; *2*] the determination of the degree to which later features of personality are related to initially selected variables; and *3*] relating the significance of any empirically determined relationship between antecedent and consequence to supposed processes in personality development. Since the object of the present chapter is to consider the relation of the requirements for the use of a longitudinal methodology to the study of behavioral development, consideration of other investigations will be selective rather than complete. Only those studies which have important implications for method will therefore be discussed.

The first decision facing any investigator who wishes to pursue a longitudinal study of psychological functions is the selection of initial variables. Whether a study is planned as a longitudinal investigation from the outset or becomes one at some date subsequent to the collection of the initial raw data, the clear definition of those features of psychological functioning which are to be studied in time or related to later features of personality organization is essential. Although the selection of initial variables can in part be viewed as a matter of taste or as determined by an investigator's particular interest, it is important that the variables be objectively observable, readily identifiable, and capable of being related to the development of psychological functions. The first two of these considerations pose only procedural difficulties. The last inevitably introduces assumptions about the developmental process which may have far-reaching effects on the entire course of the investigation.

Acceptance of psychoanalytic theory has been basic to many of the studies in the area of personality development. Starting from such a theoretical position, many workers have had to be concerned with drive states, motivation, arousal and satisfaction, affective states, psychosexual development, fantasy life, and similar categories which are fundamental to psychoanalytic theory. These variables had then to be studied in infants and young children if the longitudinal investigations were to be pertinent to the theory. However, the usual psychoanalytic techniques by means of which these features of functioning have been explored depend in largest part upon verbal communication, which is virtually absent in the behavior of young children. Consequently, direct behavioral observations, to which the study of very young children is necessarily limited, have had to be used by psychoanalysts. They have viewed such investigation as being a poor substitute for "real" psychological study.

This point of view has been expressed most clearly by René Spitz, who has stated that:

. . . in the case of the early stages of life, where the usual psychoanalytic methods of free association and verbal communication are not applicable, the experimental-psychological approach used within the framework of the psychoanalytic investigation can offer valuable contributions to the psychoanalytic theory and to the psychoanalytic clinic. It can never replace the exact psychoanalytic investigation of the given individual child with its whole background, it can only complement it. It can disclose certain regularities and point out the directions in which later psychoanalytic investigation of the individual may expect pathology. It will always have to look forward to the confirmation which can be offered by the ulterior psychoanalytic exploration of the same individuals who previously were experimental-psychologically investigated and diagnosed. It will never achieve the richness offered by psychoanalytic research nor will it be the delicate tool in the differentiation of individuals that psychoanalysis is. But within its limits and understood in its relations to psychoanalytic theory, it has valuable contributions to offer.[4]

This fundamental belief in the limited usefulness of investigations of behavioral rather than "psychological" characteristics in infants and young children has taken different form in the work of different investigators. One logical extreme is expressed in the longitudinal study conducted by Kris and his co-workers at the Yale Child Study Center. The study plan used included psychological testing of the mothers during pregnancy and repeated explorations of the mother's attitudes by social workers, both before and after the delivery. During the first two years of the child's life, the only member of the project staff who studied the children was the pediatrician, who provided baby care and administered infant developmental tests. "The analysts began to have direct contact with the children when they entered nursery school at the age of a little over two years. When the children were about three, individual explorative play contacts with the analysts were initiated, and some of the children were taken into psychoanalytic treatment." [5] Thus study of the child was delayed until language communication had become manifest in development.

It is quite clear from the study plan that no opportunity existed for defining the child's characteristics of psychological function during the first two years of life. The children did not have a significant role in the investigation until they had reached two years of age and could be studied by analytic techniques. Since the early phases of work concentrated upon details of maternal functioning and intrafamilial relationships, evidence on these matters represented the only body of systematic data available to be related to features of functioning in the children at a later age. By its very design the study predetermined that interpretations of the child's later functioning could only occur in relation to maternal attitude and intrafamilial organization. Characteristics of the child during infancy could not be considered because of the exclusion of relevant data on such functioning from the design.

Another variant of the psychoanalytic position can be found in the work of Richmond and his associates. Accepting the view that psychologically relevant observations cannot be made on infants and young children, these investigators have taken the position that "because of the infant's incapacity to communicate at a verbal level . . . studies of newborn infants can only be oriented psychologically since data collection must necessarily be physiologic [including motor development] or biochemical." [6] In practice taking this position has meant that if one cannot study psychological functions in newborn infants, the choice of what one studies should be dictated by methodologic elegance and the refinement of measures. In accordance with this view, Richmond and his associates have devoted themselves to the meticulous collection of information concerning the individual differences in such features of autonomic reactivity as heart and respiratory rates under a variety of conditions of stimulation.[7,8] Such physiologic data have been discussed by Richmond as potentially relevant to the "developmental patterns in the growing organism" and to the physiology of such aspects of emotional development as mood, affect, grief, depression, love-erotic phenomena, object relationships, separation, and the mother-infant symbiotic unit.[9] In the absence of any follow-up study of behavioral development, all such extensions are entirely presumptive. Until we have a clear-cut conception of the pertinence of such features of physiologic reactivity to the development of psychological states or to behavior, these carefully and rigorously collected physiologic data can only be speculatively extended to "adultomorphic" interpretations.[9]

Additional problems that have arisen in earlier attempts to study behavioral development are illustrated by a consideration of the prediction and outcome study conducted by Escalona and her associates.[10] In the course of a cross-sectional study of personality development, an attempt was made to delineate individual differences in the functioning of normal infants. The subjects were 128 infants comprising eight boys and eight girls studied at each four-week age level from four to thirty-two weeks. Each infant was studied under two conditions: a four-hour session at the project site, and a one-hour home visit made within ten days of the session. Additional information was obtained in the course of unsystematic encounters with other members of the family, as well as from infant testing and pediatric examination. Several years after the completion of this study, thirty-one of the *most readily available* children were selected as subjects for a "coping project." [11] The aims of this new study were the analysis of the manner in which children "cope with their own problems and to explore the relation of these efforts to aspects of temperament and resources for growth." [12] The age at initial contact with the coping project of the sixteen boys and fifteen girls ranged from two years eight months to five years six months. Information about these children was obtained by means of extensive home interviews with one or both parents, developmental and projective testing, psychiatric play sessions, Miniature Life Toy sessions, and pediatric examinations. In addition, behavioral observations were made continuously during all sessions, during trips to and from the project headquarters, and during a project party at which motion picture records were taken.

The data obtained in the coping project constituted the follow-up evidence to which Escalona sought to relate her earlier observations. Ages at follow-up and ages at the time of the determination of initial characteristics varied widely. In some instances, predictions were made from a seven-and-a-half-month-old to a two-and-a-half-year-old, and in others from a four-week-old to a five-and-a-half-year-old. The predictions therefore involved the comparison of characteristics from noncomparable base lines to noncomparable terminal ages.

At the level of data collection the Escalona study contains four inadequacies that make any valid interpretation either difficult or impossible. These are: *1]* a seven-month spread during the first year of life in ages at which data on initial functioning were collected; *2]* a failure to indicate in sufficient detail the nature of the primary data, the kind of observers who were used, and the inter- or intraobserver reliability; *3]* the use of follow-up data involving a spread of more than three years from toddler to school child in the ages of the children studied; and *4]* the selection of a sample of thirty-one children out of 128 for follow-up, with only a fortuitous basis for the selection specified. In addition to these inadequacies at the level of data collection, the validity of the study is called into question by the subjective and nonreplicable nature of the procedures used for data analysis.

At the level of initial characterization of the infant, instead of assimilating the available data to any stated scheme of analysis, Escalona "jotted down such characteristics of the child or facts and impressions about the mother and environmental factors as best served to reinforce [Escalona's] picture of the baby and to crystallize whatever seemed characteristic of him as an individual." [13] The rearousal of memory was followed by the development of "a peculiar state of mind. . . . During this period I would now remember certain moments of the original study of the child, now allow images to float through my mind which quite often pictured the imaginary preschool-ager at play, during a test, losing his temper and the like." [14] This process apparently resulted in a "vague" image of the child, which "presented itself without any conscious intent. The experience was that of emergence (not at all as from a dream but more like the impulse of a bather to turn toward the shore and terminate his swim)." [15]

The writing of predictions was "a deductive process rather than an inductive one." [16] The "imaginary child" was considered in a variety of situations of later life, and his activity level, movement patterns, and responses to behavioral demands were imagined "like looking at a model while drawing a likeness" rather than as an "intellectual exercise." [17] These activities resulted in a "somewhat disjointed series of enumerations of the " 'I expect he will . . .' type." Final formulation of the prediction involved a more "orderly thinking and the application of hypotheses." [18] These involved assumptions either as to the behavioral continuity or as to the presumed relation of earlier behavioral characteristics to later psychological functioning, e.g., "that generally low sensory thresholds in infancy may have a bearing on fantasy life and the capacity for empathy in later life." [19]

From this description of method it is apparent that the primary data represent the investigator's fantasies about the child as they relate to later facts and interpretations of his functioning. The method is entirely idiosyncratic and not consciously duplicable even by the original investigator. Were high predictive levels to be obtained, these would be relevant to the manner in which *ideas* about the child are effective predictors and not to the problem of the relation of infant *behavior* to later functioning in children. The investigators are not unaware of these weaknesses. Escalona herself points out that the "predictive statements for each child are a heterogeneous assortment including simple theoretical derivations, even simpler empirical observations which were merely extended and applied to the child in question, and a peculiar variety of focused fantasy products which often reached some degree of complexity." [20] She further states the "predictions took this shape not because I thought this good scientific procedure but because I could not do it in any other way. . . ." [21]

The studies in prediction conducted by John Benjamin [22] at the University of Colorado pose similar methodological problems. In these investigations the children were studied by means of a series of play sessions, psychological tests, and psychoanalytically orientated interviews. The parents were also studied, utilizing psychoanalytic techniques. In the course of these contacts the investigators formulated predictions concerning later features of functioning in the children. These predictions were made at multiple points during the child's life, ranging from the prenatal period to early adolescence. Further, predictions were not formulated at the same time for all the children, but rather the development of any given prediction was a process unique to the particular child under study. The content of the predictions, too, varied from child to child. In fact, the instructions to the investigators included the specific warning that "because it seems possible to make a prediction in a specific area in one or more cases, it does not necessarily follow that the same area can be made the object of meaningful prediction in every child or parent in [the] sample." [23]

The predictive statements were for the most part concerned with the elaboration of certain psychoanalytic concepts. For example: "If the first child is a boy, the father's demands on him will be so great in terms of using him as a defense against his own severe castration anxiety that serious difficulties for the child may be confidently predicted"; or "Predict that Bobby will show strong eight months anxiety"; or "Predict behavioral evidences of anal retention during periods of bowel training and development of retentive derivatives in adult personality"; or "Predict that separation anxiety and its derivative manifestations will be relatively higher than castration fear and its derivatives, when [there is] clear evidence of both"; or "Predict that Mary's strong cophrophagic impulses will persist as part of her unconscious motivational system." [24]

Since the predictions concerned features of functioning at widely different ages, some predictions being of an immediate or short-term nature and others discussing functioning in adulthood, efforts at validation necessarily occurred at different points in time in the different children under study. In discussing the procedures utilized to test the validity of a prediction, Benjamin stated that it was preferred to "give overt behavioral criteria for intrapsychic variables whenever possible." [25] In other words, validation became dependent upon the interpretations given to the overt behaviors rather than on the behaviors themselves. The following example is illustrative of this technique. The prediction that a child will show "clear-cut developmental difficulties which can be specifically related to problems of feminine identification [although] . . . the mother-child relationship during early infancy should be a smooth one" [26] is judged correct on the basis of the following evidence obtained from a variety of sources, including the results of infant testing, observations during testing, impressions and interpretations of play sessions, parental reports, and the like: "*1*] Flourishing early infancy till 10½ months of age; *2*] Excessive timidity late in the first year and thereafter; *3*] High overt anxiety rating during preschool period; *4*] Characterized as passive and clinging by observer; *5*] During period between 4½ and 5 plus years development of severe 'baby talk' speech disturbance . . . ; 6] Much taking of female [Mother's and sister's] roles in play sessions, in spontaneous play as observed and reported at home." [27]

The question may be raised as to the pertinence of this "evidence" to the prediction "of clear-cut developmental difficulties which are specifically related to problems of female identification." If the prediction is to be considered correct, it must be shown that: *1*] there are clear-cut developmental difficulties; *2*] the child does indeed have a female identification; and *3*] these are specifically related. Apparently it is the descriptions of "anxiety," "timidity," "passive and clinging behavior," and "speech disturbances" that are interpreted as evidence for "clear-cut developmental difficulties." One may question whether any of these disturbances are specifically developmental in origin. Secondly, in view of Benjamin's statement that validation is to be based upon overt behavioral evidence, it should be pointed out that anxiety does not constitute a description of behavior, but rather is an interpretation of behavior. While it may be entirely justifiable in certain circumstances to engage in the making of behavioral interpretations, these interpretations should not be confused with the facts of behavior. This confusion of fact and interpretation pervades the presentation of the data in the Benjamin study. Predictions, too, are formulated in theoretical and interpretive terms. Their validation rests not on objective behavioral evidence, but rather on the interpretation of behavior within a given theoretical system. If in these circumstances a prediction is judged correct, it is possible that the accuracy of the prediction results from the operation of a systematic interpretive bias, rather than from objective evidence. When one considers the Benjamin study in the light of the previously stated criteria for longitudinal study, it is obvious that it meets none of them. The initial behaviors are not identified, the age base varies from fetal life to adolescence, the interpretation is substituted for fact, and the content of the later behavior is determined on an *ad hoc* basis.

Meili [28] approached the problem of the study of personality development from an entirely different vantage point. He stated that the aim of his investigation was to

study a fully developed personality not through a hypothetical reconstruction of its development but rather through participation as it were in its formation. Thus, a longitudinal study was planned in which children were to be studied and observed at regular intervals from the time of birth on. At each examination the psychological characteristics of the subject, particularly as they were relevant to personality development, were to be carefully investigated. The study was then to determine how far these successive vignettes of a personality were in accord, and how frequently new personality traits were encountered which could not definitely be said to have derived from those previously existing. [29]

To this end Meili studied twenty-six normal children from birth through five and six years of life. These children were seen on two occasions during the first month, once a month till they reached six months, every other month until the second year, every fourth month until the third year, and every sixth month thereafter. Studies were conducted in the homes of the children, and the sources of information were: *1]* a relatively brief and unstructured interview with the mother concerning certain limited features of the child's everyday behavior; and 2] the child's performance in a series of "experiments." These experiments consisted of a series of stimulus-response situations which differed at different age levels. For example, in very young children the behavior during feeding was observed. In the period from one to six months responses to objects moving across the visual field were studied, and in the second half of the first year and beyond tasks were selected to correspond as closely as possible to the expected level of response. All of these experiments were filmed. In the first four months a fifteen-meter reel, permitting the recording of approximately two minutes of action, was used. In the older children the length was doubled.

Several problems arise regarding these techniques of data collection. Although the stated objective of the study was to obtain information regarding the child's functioning in his normal, everyday environment, Meili chose to ignore the parents as a source of behavioral information on the grounds that it would be too time-consuming and demanding to conduct detailed parental interviews. Instead, the children's reactions to what are essentially standard test situations, rather than situations of daily life, were recorded on motion picture film. Of necessity there is introduced a highly artificial set of stimulational and observational circumstances, the relation of which to normal conditions of functioning can only be inferred with difficulty. This difficulty is compounded by the fact that the observational data at each age level are concerned with a period of only two to four minutes.

It is, however, at the level of data analysis that the most serious problems arise concerning the Meili study. It will be recalled that Meili sought to use observational data as the basis for "deriving the traits characteristic of each child at each stage of development." He chose to do this, however, by treating the motion picture records as if they were the protocols of projective tests, stating that the available records "cannot be used as direct indications of what the child is like; instead the observed pattern of behavior must be interpreted." [30] This position results in the data being treated within the framework of an untestable systematic bias. Even the tentative conclusions proposed and recognized by

Meili to be in need of further verification may be the result of the bias, ubiquitously present, in the analysis of the data obtained at different age levels. Although the objectives of the Meili study are in accord with the criteria for longitudinal study, the techniques employed in the collection and analyses of data are somewhat less than satisfactory.

It is against the background of this selective review of longitudinal investigations * that one can reformulate the necessary conditions for sound longitudinal study of personality development. They consist of:

1] The identification of initial characteristics that may be objectively and reliably studied in infants and young children.
2] The development of techniques for data collection that will permit the obtaining of objective data pertinent to the question under study.
3] The establishment of the reliability of the data-collecting techniques.
4] The development of objective methods of data analysis that are subject to verification.
5] The study of the continuity of these initial characteristics, utilizing objective and reliable techniques for data analysis at each age level.
6] The identification of new features of functional organization as they appear.
7] The development of similar measures of objectivity and reliability for the study and analysis of these later phenomena.
8] The relating of the initial characteristics to the later described features of functional organization.

This book is concerned with only the first phases of a longitudinal study of behavioral development. The following chapters discuss the identification of initial characteristics and the develop-

---

* *Birth to Maturity; A Study in Psychological Development,* by J. Kagan and H. A. Moss (New York: John Wiley, 1962), which reports the carefully analyzed data of the long-term longitudinal study of the Fels Institute, appeared too late to be included in this selective review of the literature.

ment of objective, reliable, and verifiable techniques for data collection and analysis. Information concerning the continuity of these initial characteristics is presented. The problem of identifying later features of functional organization and their relation to initially defined characteristics will be dealt with in subsequent reports.

REFERENCES

1. D. Kodlin and D. J. Thompson, "An Appraisal of the Longitudinal Approach to Studies of Growth and Development," Monographs of the Society for Research in Child Development, 23: No. 1 (1958), 8.

2. A. Stone and G. Onqué, *Longitudinal Studies of Child Personality* (Cambridge: Harvard University Press, 1959).

3. S. Escalona and others, "Early Phases of Personality Development: A Non-Normative Study of Infant Behavior," Monographs of the Society for Research in Child Development, 17: No. 1 (1952), 25.

4. R. Spitz, "Relevancy of Direct Infant Observation," *Psychoanalytic Study of the Child*, 5:66 (1950).

5. M. Kris, "The Use of Prediction in a Longitudinal Study," *Psychoanalytic Study of the Child*, 12:175 (1957).

6. J. B. Richmond and E. L. Lipton, "Some Aspects of the Neurophysiology of the Newborn and Their Implications for Child Development," *Dynamic Psychopathology in Childhood*, eds. L. Jessner and E. Pavenstedt (New York: Grune and Stratton, 1959), p. 78.

7. E. L. Lipton, J. B. Richmond, and S. L. Lustman, "Autonomic Function in the Neonate and Psychosomatic Disease," *American Journal of Diseases of Children*, 90:491 (1955).

8. E. L. Lipton, A. Steinschneider, and J. B. Richmond, "Autonomic Function in the Neonate," *Psychosomatic Medicine*, 23:472 (1961).

9. Richmond and Lipton, *op. cit.*, pp. 78–79.

10. S. Escalona and G. M. Heider, *Prediction and Outcome: A Study in Child Development* (New York: Basic Books, 1959).

11. L. B. Murphy, "The Child's Way of Coping: A Longitudinal Study of Normal Children," Bulletin of the Menninger Clinic, 24:97 (1960).

12. Escalona and Heider, *op. cit.*, p. 18.

13. *Ibid.*, p. 22.

14. *Ibid.*, p. 23.

15. *Ibid.*

16. *Ibid.*

17. *Ibid.*

18. *Ibid.,* p. 24.

19. *Ibid.*

20. *Ibid.,* p. 22.

21. *Ibid.*

22. J. D. Benjamin, "Prediction and Psychopathologic Theory," *Dynamic Psychopathology in Childhood,* eds. L. Jessner and E. Pavenstedt, *op. cit.*

23. *Ibid.,* p. 13.

24. *Ibid.,* pp. 25, 36, 40, 46, 56.

25. *Ibid.,* p. 23.

26. *Ibid.,* p. 25.

27. *Ibid.,* p. 26.

28. R. Meili, "A Longitudinal Study of Personality Development," *Dynamic Psychopathology in Childhood,* eds. L. Jessner and E. Pavenstedt, *op. cit.*

29. *Ibid.,* p. 106.

30. *Ibid.*

III

Data Collection

SINCE THE parental reports represent the major source for behavioral information during the first two years of the child's life, it is necessary to consider some of the questions relevant to the use of material obtained through parental interviews. One tends to approach the parent as a valid source of information on development with considerable skepticism. A number of studies [1,2] have impugned parental report because the normal propensity for memory to be modified by patterns of needs and motives may result in systematic distortions in the reporting of behavioral data. However, in our analysis of these criticisms we were impressed by two features of the evidence which, if properly assessed, suggested strongly that the parents might be utilized as both a valid and reliable source of behavioral information. First, it was clear that the accuracy of the parent as a reporter of behavioral events was affected by the distance in time of the interview from the event described. Second, the degree of distortion of the report appeared to be markedly influenced by the degree of specificity and objectivity of the questions asked.[3,4,5] Both factors provided grounds for anticipating that if interviews were conducted at sufficiently short intervals, and if the questions asked of the parent referred to concrete objective behaviors rather than to complex motives and other subjective states, the parents could, in fact, be a most useful source of behavioral information.

From a methodologic point of view, therefore, the problem

of utilizing the parent as a basic data source boiled down to the determination of the adequacy of the parent as a source for detailed behavioral information. The answer could only be obtained empirically. It required that a group of parents be selected and interviewed concerning the behavioral development of the child. The interview used had to satisfy the criteria of concreteness and closeness in time to the behavior to be described. The data sought from the parents were the facts of behavior given descriptively. The prime emphasis was on *how* the baby behaved in specific situations. Special attention was paid to responses to the child's first contact with a new stimulus, such as a new food. Also explored in detail were the responses made to the same stimulus on subsequent exposures until a consistent, long-term pattern of response had emerged. In addition, questions were asked about the occurrence of any subsequent situations which changed or modified this consistent response, either temporarily or permanently.

Despite the character of the interview many parents gave an interpretation when the question called for an objective description of behavior. Whenever this occurred the question was repeated and rephrased until an actual description of behavior was obtained. For example:

INTERVIEWER: "What did the baby do the first time he was given cereal?"

PARENT: "He liked it," "He loved it," "He couldn't stand it," "It wasn't sweet enough," "It was too thick," "He wasn't used to the consistency," "He had to become familiar with it," etc.

All these reports represent interpretations of the behavior rather than descriptions. The interpretations may even be accurate. However, in each case a specific, step-by-step description was insisted on. Thus:

INTERVIEWER: "What makes you think he disliked it? What did he do?"

PARENT: "He spit it out and when another spoonful was offered he turned his head to the side."

While interpretation was not accepted as a substitute for description, interpretations were recorded. However, in assessing the behavior of the child, only behaviorally descriptive data were used for scoring.

Before being interviewed, the parents were told that this was a project to study the individual behavior of normal children in normal homes and that they should not deviate in any way from their usual procedure of handling the child nor keep any special records. It was emphasized that the study did not involve making value judgments on the merits of a particular baby's behavior and that the data obtained would not be analyzed in terms of any hierarchy of desirability. The interviewer, it was explained, would not tell the parents what conclusions were being drawn from the data, since such information could influence the objectivity of their report.

The first interview occurred when the child was approximately three months old, and a general outline was used in order to obtain both background and behavioral information. The main areas covered are described below.

1] *Siblings.* Number, sex, ages.

2] *Brief obstetrical history.* Full term or otherwise, complications of pregnancy, delivery, or postpartum.

3] *Neonatal.* Birth weight and length, any unusual circumstances or physical disturbances.

4] *Responsibility for the daily care of the baby.* In what degree are various adults involved in the child's care (mother, father, other relatives, nurse)?

5] *Parental description of the child's personality.* This question was not asked to obtain objective data, but as a possible clue to parental attitude. It was asked in a nondirective manner, as an open-ended question. The parents' answers were recorded verbatim, and no attempt was made to develop or discuss the answer. The question was posed along the following lines: "If a friend or relative who had never seen the baby asked you to describe his personality, what would you say?"

6] *Details of daily living:*

A. *Sleep*. This item is closely related to the feeding behavior in the first weeks of life, since periods of wakefulness and hunger on the one hand, and satiation and sleep on the other hand, appear to be functionally interdependent. Therefore, data on sleep in this period usually had to include data on feeding as well. Pertinent material involved duration of periods of sleeping and wakefulness, regularity or irregularity of these periods, behavior in going to sleep and waking up, and the amount of motor activity and vocalization during sleep. Inasmuch as the sleep pattern usually changes rapidly in the first weeks of life, the history of this period was broken down into short intervals. If any data were available as to the sleeping pattern in the hospital's newborn nursery, this was recorded. Questions were asked regarding the response of the sleeping pattern to: *1*] any modification in handling by the parent; *2*] any unusual circumstances, such as an upper respiratory infection or travel away from home; and *3*] handling by different people.

B. *Feeding.* *1*] Bottle- or breast-fed, or combination of the two? *2*] Self-demand, schedule, or modified self-demand? *3*] Feeding schedule time interval, regularity or irregularity in time and amount, pattern of change of schedule as baby grew older, reaction to any special circumstances, such as noise, illness, or travel away from home? *4*] What parental attempts were made to modify the schedule and what was the baby's response to such attempts? For example, if the baby was awakened for feeding at 10:00 P.M. in the hope of eliminating the 2:00 A.M. awakening, what was his response on being awakened? What was this feeding like, and how did it change or modify the 2:00 A.M. and later morning awakening? *5*] How did the baby indicate hunger? Did he cry? What was the intensity of crying? Was there a quick or slow building up of crying? How easily was crying stopped or diminished by such devices as holding the baby? Was there evidence of conditioning, such as the stopping of crying with one of the specific prefeeding maneuvers, e.g., putting the bib on? 6] How did the baby indicate satiation? 7] If feeding was interrupted, for instance, for burping, did he fuss, cry, or show no reaction? Did he have a pattern of pausing in the middle of a feeding, and did he develop such a pattern quickly, slowly, or not at all? 8] Was the amount of food intake regular at each feeding? 9] Was the sucking pattern desultory, mild, or vigorous? What use was made of pacifiers, and were they effective in stopping crying? 10] Was there any difference in the feeding pattern when the child was fed by different individuals? 11] What was the response to vitamin drops, and how were they initially administered? What were the first and subsequent responses observed until a consistent long-term response was established? Did the baby let it dribble out or did he swallow it? Did he lick his lips? Did he smile or have any other facial expression? Did he whine or cry? Did he turn his head toward or away from the dropper or spoon? Did he open or close his mouth at the approach of the dropper or spoon? Was any difference in response observed by changing the type or form of preparation used, or by using an admixture with another food? 12] Orange juice—same questions as with vitamin drops. 13] Solid foods—in general, same questions as with vitamin drops. The interviewer noted the time sequence of starting various solids, the baby's response to each of the first five or six solids started, and to subsequent ones where there was any different type of reaction. His food preferences and dislikes were noted. The parent was asked whether there was a pattern of alternation of milk and solid foods, and if so, whether the practice was rigid or flexible (e.g., two sucks of milk and a swallow of solid, all of solid and then entire bottle, etc.). What was the infant's reaction if the usual alternation of milk and solid at each meal was modified? 14] If the infant was initially breast-fed, what was his reaction to milk from the bottle on the first occasion and on subsequent occasions? If he was both breast- and bottle-fed, was his behavior the same or different during the two types of feeding?

15] Was there a difference in response to the bottle if it contained milk, orange juice, or water?

C. *Soiling and wetting.* *1*] Did the baby show any reaction to being wet or soiled? What did he do? *2*] If he showed a characteristic reaction, such as fussing, did this stop only when he was clean or dry, or did he stop at some specific points in the process of changing him? *3*] How many bowel movements did he have daily? Were they regular and at regular times? Did he have any consistent type of overt reaction to the passage or presence of the stool?

D. *Bath.* *1*] At what age was the first bath given, and how did the baby react? *2*] Was there a change from his first reaction at subsequent baths? If so, was this a gradual or an abrupt change? *3*] What was the time relationship of bath to feeding? Was there any change in reaction to the bath if the time relationship to feeding was changed? *4*] Did he behave differently in a different bathtub or if the bath was given by a different person? *5*] If there was a bath-free interval of several days or longer, e.g., during illness, what was the infant's reaction to the resumption of the bath?

E. *Nailcutting.* Description of behavior on first and subsequent occasions.

F. *Hairbrushing.* Same as for nailcutting.

G. *Washing of face, hair, nose, and ears.* Same as for nailcutting.

H. *Doctor.* Reaction to doctor and to examination by doctor. Description of immediate reaction to each injection. How loud was the cry? How long did it last? What stopped it? Was there any difference between the first and subsequent examinations and immunizations? On the second or later visits was there any reaction upon coming into the doctor's office, seeing the doctor, being undressed, or being placed on the table preliminary to the examination?

I. *Dressing and undressing.* What was the response to dressing or any specific aspect of it, such as pulling the shirt over the head? Was the baby's reaction consistent? Did it vary with the time of day or with the person dressing him?

J.   *Sensory.* 1] Could the parent estimate whether the child was more sensitive to one class of stimuli, e.g., visual or auditory, and less to another? 2] What was the reaction to loud noise or to sudden noise, such as the doorbell? Was there a startle reaction and/or a cry? What was the intensity and duration of these? How did the pattern of response change as the baby grew older? 3] What was the response to bright light? Was the child attracted by it? Did he squint or cry? Did he turn his head toward or away from it? If he was already crying, did the putting on of the light or the making of sounds stop crying or intensify it?

K.   *Motility.* General description of level of motility. Could the parents estimate whether the baby was active, moderate, or quiet? Description of movements during sleep. Did the infant sleep on his belly or back? How did the baby indicate preference, if any? How much movement was there in the crib? Was he found at different places in the crib? Did he squirm during feeding? In addition, motility data were obtained during inquiries about dressing, bathing, feeding, play, etc.

L.   *Response to people.* At what age was the first differentiated response to a person noted? What was it? A description of subsequent differentiating behavior was elicited.

M.   *Response to illness.* The specific change in behavior during illness. Did behavior return to the preillness pattern immediately after the illness was over? If not, what differences persisted and for how long?

N.   *Crying.* Enumerate the specific types of situations that made him cry. What made him stop? How long did he cry? How loudly did he cry?

O.   Is there anything you can think of that should be mentioned about your baby's behavior that has been omitted?

Subsequent interviews were conducted at three-month intervals through the first year and then at six-month intervals. In the later interviews items of behavior recorded in earlier histories that were still pertinent to present functioning were again recorded, together with detailed descriptions of any changes that had occurred. New items were added as they appeared in the child's functioning, such as play patterns, response to training and learning of limits, attempts to dress himself, etc. The following list indicates the nature of modifications introduced in interviews subsequent to the first:

A. *Sleep.* Time and regularity of bedtime and nap time. Did the child go to sleep easily or not? Was there any special ritual at bedtime? Did he sleep through the night? If he awakened at night, what was the frequency, what was the behavior on awakening, and what was required to put him back to sleep? What was the response to any parental attempt to modify the sleep pattern? Did the sleep pattern change with illness, teething, or change of surroundings? If so, what was the change, and how quickly did it revert to the previous pattern when the apparent cause of the change disappeared? What was the behavior on awakening?

B. *Feeding.* Amount and regularity of food intake, response to new foods, consistency of likes and dislikes. When and how did he initiate attempts to feed himself? How persistent was he? What was his reaction to difficulty in using a spoon? Did he allow the mother to feed him, or had he started feeding himself? If he fed himself, did he also allow adults to feed him? Describe in detail his reaction to weaning from the breast or bottle. How was his feeding affected by teething or illness?

C. *Soiling and wetting.* Same questions as in first interview. When was toilet training started? What were the techniques used? What was the child's reaction to attempts at bowel and bladder training? Describe the sequences of behavior in detail.

D. *Bath.* What was his behavior when he heard bath water running? What was his behavior in the bath? Did he object to removal from the bath? Was there a reaction to any change in the bathtub or the person bathing him? At what age did he attempt to wash himself? When this occurred what was his reaction to his mother's washing him? What was his reaction to a hairwash?

E.   *Nailcutting, hairbrushing, washing of face, nose, ears, and hands.*   Same as for bath. What were his reactions? Did he attempt to do any of these things by himself? If so, how? Did he request help? Did he accept help?

F.   *Doctor.*   Same as in first interview.

G.   *Dressing and undressing.*   Did he resist, cooperate, or do neither? Did he resist being held still? At what age did he attempt to dress himself? Once this occurred, how persistent was he? What were his responses to the difficulties?

H.   *Sensory.*   How long did the startle reaction persist? What was the specific reaction? Could the parents make any estimate of the baby's relative responsiveness to different sensory modalities? What was his reaction to pain? Did sound or light easily disturb his sleep?

I.   *Neuromuscular.*   When did each new development occur, e.g., sitting and walking? Did mastery of the activity come suddenly or after a period of persistent effort? What was the child's reaction to failure in his effort at mastery? What was his reaction when success was achieved? Once he was walking and climbing actively, did he avoid obstacles and danger? Did he fall frequently or rarely? Was a playpen used? During the period when a playpen was used, how did he react to being placed in it, and how long did he stay in it? How did he indicate a wish to get out of the playpen?

J.   *Response to people.*   What was the reaction to strangers? Did he take the initiative, respond quickly to a stranger's initiative, require a period of warming up, or show a general negative reaction? Did he show any special responses to any specific people, strange or familiar? What were his responses to the various members of the family? What happened when one or both of his parents left the house? If one or both parents were away for any period of time, what were his specific behavioral changes during their absence and on their return? What was the baby's behavior with any older sibling? If a new sibling was born, describe his reactions in detail and in sequence. What was his behavior with older and younger children, as well as with those of his own age?

K.   *Response to illness.*   Same as in first interview.

L.   *Play.*   How long did he play alone? How long did he concentrate on one toy or game? What were his favorite toys? If a toy or game was too difficult, did he persist, give up easily, call for help, cry, have a tantrum, throw or destroy the toy? Did he take to a new toy or game with people quickly or did he prefer the more familiar toys and games? What was the pattern of play with adults, older children, and children of his own age? What was his reaction when a toy was grabbed from him by another child? Did he grab toys from other children? Did he make games out of activities with people? If so, what were the specific patterns?

M.   *Learning of limits.*   What was his response to a parental "No" or spanking? How quickly and easily could he be trained to avoid a prohibited item or activity? If forcibly moved from an activity, what was his reaction? How easily could he be distracted? How easily could he be trained to do specific tasks, such as putting toys away?

N.   *Verbalizations.*   Did he babble? When did he start? How much did he babble? When did he first use words, phrases, sentences? During the period of language development how much did he practice with new sounds and words? How much did he imitate words of other people? How much did he use verbalization in his interpersonal contacts and in other activities?

O.   *Crying.*   What made him cry? What made him stop? If he hurt himself, what was the crying pattern?

P.   *Haircut.*   What was his behavior on his first haircut and on subsequent ones until a consistent reaction was established?

The interviews were structured but flexible, and questioning was semischeduled. Each interview lasted from one to two hours during the first year and from two to four hours during the second year of life. The responses were recorded during the interview and transcribed immediately thereafter.

REFERENCES

1. F. C. Bartlett, *Remembering: A Study in Experimental and Social Psychology* (Cambridge: Cambridge University Press, 1932).
2. E. G. Schachtel, "On Memory and Childhood Amnesia," *Psychiatry*, 10:1 (1947).
3. E. A. Haggard, A. Brekstad, and A. G. Skard, "On the Reliability of the Anamnestic Interview," *Journal of Abnormal and Social Psychology*, 61:311 (1960).
4. K. E. Goddard, G. Broder, and C. Wenar, "Reliability of Pediatric Histories. A Preliminary Study," *Pediatrics*, 28:1011 (1961).
5. M. K. Pyles, H. R. Stoltz, and J. W. MacFarlane, "The Accuracy of Mothers' Reports on Birth and Development Data," *Child Development*, 6:165 (1935).

IV

Subjects and Procedures for Data Treatment

THE PRESENT REPORT is concerned with the data collected on the first 80 of the 130 children whose behavioral development has been followed from the first months of life. These 80 children are those of the group who had passed their second birthdays at the time the present analysis was undertaken. Thirty-nine of the children were girls and 41 were boys.

The families of all the children represent a fairly homogeneous middle- and upper-middle-class urban and suburban group. The group is predominantly Jewish, with some Catholic and Protestant families. There is one Negro and one Chinese family. Almost all parents were born in the United States, and all are residents of the greater New York area. At the time of the child's birth half of the mothers were less than 31 years old, with an age range of 20 to 41 years. The median age of the fathers was 33.6 years, with the youngest 25 years and the oldest 54 years. The length of marriage at the child's birth ranged from one to 19 years, with half of the group married at least 5.3 years. The educational backgrounds of the parents were fairly similar. Seventy-five percent of the mothers and 82 percent of the fathers had a college education and postgraduate degrees, and only about 10 percent had no college at all. A summary of the occupational fields of the mothers and fathers is presented in Table 1.

Some of the mothers have continued in their occupations following the birth of the child or have resumed them on a full-

TABLE 1

OCCUPATIONS OF PARENTS

	Mothers	Fathers
Academic		
College professor	2	6
Schoolteacher	14	3
Miscellaneous (piano or dancing teacher, etc.)	3	1
Business		
Manager, executive	2	6
Secretary	13	0
Miscellaneous (salesman, insurance adjuster, etc.)	2	5
Creative		
Artist	3	1
Theater	4	8
Writer, editor, publisher	2	3
Professional		
Lawyer	2	8
Physician	3	10
Psychologist	3	3
Social worker	6	1
Miscellaneous (pharmacist, optometrist, nurse, etc.)	3	7
Miscellaneous (union official, bartender, machinist, etc.)	3	3
Total	65	65

(Fifteen of these parents have two children each in the study population of eighty children. The other fifty parents have one child each in the study.)

time (5 percent) or part-time (32 percent) basis by the time the child was two years old. However, the mothers uniformly described their major responsibility as being the care of the children. Many of the fathers participated actively in the care of the child. Reported child care practices were highly similar within the group, with emphasis placed on the importance of satisfying the baby's needs. Child care, as reported by the parents, generally conformed to the practices recommended by Spock (in *Baby and Child Care*) and other such common sources of child-rearing advice. With almost no exceptions the mothers in this group were oriented to the self-demand approach to feeding; and approximately 50 percent breast-fed their infants and used supplementary bottle feedings. The shift to the exclusive use of bottles was gradually accomplished during the first two to five months. Weaning from the bottle was started when the child was between five and eleven months of age, and by the end of twenty-four months more than 50 percent of the children were completely weaned.

In the approach to toilet training a generally permissive attitude was reported. The parents did not press vigorously for the establishment of early training. Only 20 percent of the parents started training below twelve months of age. Half of the group did not begin any systematic bowel or bladder training until the children were at least sixteen months old. In most cases training was completed between eighteen and thirty-six months, and in a few children training was not successfully completed until the fourth year.

Other events may be noted to help characterize the environment of this group of children. The subsequent birth of a younger sibling occurred in approximately one third of the families. Hospitalization for various illnesses or operative procedures during the first two years was reported for 10 percent of the children. Separation or divorce of the parents occurred in 8 percent of the families, in every case before the children studied were two years of age.

The group of eighty includes five sets of twins. Twenty-eight, or 35 percent of the children, were the first born, and thirteen remained the only child through at least their second year. An additional thirteen, or 16 percent of the children, have two or more older siblings, and seven of the children reside in households that include children of previous marriages of one or both parents.

The initial contacts with the families, which arranged for their participation in the study, were often made before the birth of the child or within the first weeks after birth. The first behavior interview, where the initial history detailing the behavior of the infant in daily activities was recorded, was carried out within the first four months after birth in all but 14 percent of the eighty children. The average age of the children described in the first parental report was 3.3 months, and at that point half of the children were less than 2.5 months of age. Subsequent histories were taken at approximately three-month intervals for a year, then at six-month intervals. Some slight deviation from a rigidly maintained schedule occurred because of the lack of availability of the parent due to illness, vacation trips, and other special circumstances.

For data analysis each child's record was subdivided into five age groups (I through V), representing successive intervals covered by separate parental reports. The selection of these five periods was governed by the pattern of data collection. The primary consideration was an attempt to select relatively brief periods in infancy during which new child care situations would arise, e.g., feeding, bathing, dress. Activities underwent changes as the child grew. In this manner the description of the children's behavior was based on broader repertories of activities in an increasing variety of situations. During some periods and with many children, more than one parental report was obtained. The scores of any multiple interviews on the same child were simply combined. The sums of all the respective scored items were entered as the behavior record for the particular age period. The average ages of the children at the end of each of the five data-treatment periods are enumerated in Table 2.

TABLE 2

AGE AT TERMINATION OF PERIOD
(In Months)

Age Period	Mean	Median	Summation of Data
I	5.9	5.4	1.8
II	11.2	11.3	1.9
III	15.5	15.6	2.8
IV	21.2	20.1	3.9
V	27.3	26.5	4.6

As may be seen from Table 2, period I of data treatment included the first six months of the child's development. It therefore represents in the majority of the cases the combining of the parental report covering the first three months of life with the report dealing with the second three months. The reason for this summation of data derives from the fact that fourteen of the first eighty cases were included in the study after they had reached the age of three months. In order to include these children, it was necessary to take their age at inclusion in the study as the lower limit of initial categorization. Period I, then, includes descriptions of the children's behavior from birth to an average age of 5.9 months. The scores for Period II include reports of behavior from the termination of the preceding period up to the average age of 11.2 months. The same procedure was maintained for the determination of each of the subsequent age periods.

METHOD OF BEHAVIOR ANALYSIS

Given a body of detailed behavioral information, several models may be used in analyzing the data for purposes of longitudinal study. In the first instance, the data may be analyzed from the point of view of a given theory of developmental interrelations. One viewpoint may dictate concentration upon the phenomena of alimentation and elimination as crucial determinants of later psychological functioning. Another view, concerning itself with the energetics of activity per se, may concentrate primarily on the intensity of response. A third model which may be used is that of selecting indicator behaviors, such as clinging, grasping, and ease or difficulty of satiation or arousal, as prognosticators of specific subsequent characteristics of personality organization. Although each of these approaches has a certain value, it is clear that each deals with only a selected fragment, and a deductively determined one at that, of the totality of behavioral data available both from parental interview and from direct observation of children. Clearly, any analysis of data other than the mere restatement of the behaviors themselves is the result of a selective process and as such cannot embrace every datum. It was therefore necessary in the present study to decide upon a method of analysis that broadly encompassed the behavioral data yet avoided the noncategorical and diffuse character of mere behavioral restatement. It was possible to achieve this by the inductive content analysis of the behavior protocols, obtaining through such analysis a set of formal categories to which the behavioral data could be assimilated. The obvious approach to the development of such formal categories was a content analysis.

A content analysis was therefore performed on the interview protocols of the first twenty-two children studied. In the course of this analysis the protocol data were distributed against a wide variety of formal behavioral attributes. It was found that nine categories of functioning could be scored continuously throughout the protocols. Further, the distributions of scores in each of these categories were sufficiently wide to permit differentiation among individuals within each category. Although various amounts of data were available for additional categories of functioning, their distributions failed to satisfy either the requirement of ubiquitousness (being scorable and present in all protocols), or of sufficient variability to permit of interindividual comparison. The content analysis, therefore, resulted in the adoption of the following nine categories for the assessment of individuality in behavioral functioning:

1] Activity level

The motor component present in a given child's functioning, and the diurnal proportion of active and inactive periods, plus protocol data on motility during bathing, eating, playing, dressing, and handling, as well as information concerning the sleep-wake cycle, reaching, crawling, and walking, were used in scoring this category.

2] Rhythmicity

The predictability and/or the unpredictability in time of any function was analyzed in relation to the sleep-wake cycle, hunger, feeding pattern, and elimination schedule.

3] *Approach or withdrawal*

The nature of the response to a new stimulus, be it a new food, new toy, or new person, provided information relevant to this category.

4] *Adaptability*

Responses to new or altered situations. One is not concerned with the nature of the initial responses, but with the frequency with which they were successfully modified in desired directions.

5] *Intensity of reaction*

The energy level of response, irrespective of its quality or direction.

6] *Threshold of responsiveness*

The intensity level of stimulation that was necessary to evoke a discernible response, irrespective of the specific form that the response might take or the sensory modality affected. The behaviors utilized were those concerning reactions to sensory stimuli, environmental objects, and social contacts.

7] *Quality of mood*

The amount of pleasant, joyful, and friendly behavior, as contrasted with unpleasant, crying, and unfriendly behavior.

8] *Distractibility*

The effectiveness of extraneous environmental stimuli in interfering with, or in altering the direction of, the ongoing behavior.

9]   *Attention span and persistence*

These two categories are related. Attention span is the length of time a particular activity is pursued by the child. Persistence refers to the continuation of an activity in the face of obstacles to the maintenance of the activity direction.

Once these nine categories were established a scoring procedure based on a five-point scale was developed. However, initial reliability studies indicated low reliability for middle-category positions. As a consequence, a three-point scale was adopted for use in the final scoring procedure. The three points selected for each category of behavioral functioning were the polar extremes and a middle level. Therefore, every behavioral record was scored for each of the nine categories on a three-point scale and resulted in a specific item sum for each category of reactivity. An example of a final record for the five age period subdivisions is presented in Table 3 (see p. 57).

Each protocol was analyzed for each category independently. No successive interviews of a given child were scored continuously. This segmented scoring was used to avoid contamination by halo effects, whereby the scorer's judgment on any one category or age period interview might be influenced by a judgment already made on another.

In the scoring of data, as well as in its acquisition, use was made of objective descriptive items. Interpretation was avoided. For example, the statement "He cried because he was hungry" was scored only in relation to crying. The child might or might not have been hungry, but there is no doubt that he did cry. In training scorers it was found that disagreements most frequently arose from attempts to score behavioral descriptions that were not sufficiently explicit. In such instances, the scorer had to base his judgment on an interpretation of what the statement might mean, since the ambiguity of the report made it impossible to determine the exact meaning. This difficulty was eliminated by strict adherence to the rule that any item where the description was ambiguous or vague was not to be scored.

A few typical behavior items and their scoring may now be given to illustrate the general approach. The item "He lies quietly in the bath and doesn't kick" is scored as low activity level. "He ate cereal well the first time I gave it to him" is scored as an approach response. "At first he spit out his egg, but after the third time he took it" is scored as high adaptability. "When the bell rang he jumped and cried" is scored as low threshold of responsiveness. Single behavioral items are frequently scorable in two or more categories. For example, the statement "He kicks wildly, gurgles happily, and laughs loudly in his bath and has done so from the very first time" can be scored as: *1*] high activity level; *2*] initial approach; *3*] positive mood; and *4*] intense response. "He kicks and whimpers when he has his nails cut, but if we talk to him or show him a toy, he is quiet" is scored as: *1*] high activity level; *2*] negative mood; *3*] mild intensity; and *4*] distractibility.

As would be expected, parents of different children differed markedly in the quality of their spontaneous descriptions of their children's behavior. Some were factual and objective, others were subjective and interpretative, or largely concerned with value judgments; some were concise and others rambled. There was also great variation in the amount of detail given regarding various features of behavior. However, our interview technique, in which we demanded answers in terms of specific factual details of behavior, elicited a great deal of objective data even from mothers who were spontaneously subjective, interpretative, preoccupied with value judgments, or who rambled or otherwise tended to report insufficient descriptive items. The factual data from any one interview could be broken down into an average of sixty to seventy scorable items of behavior.

In practice every protocol was scored as follows: Each of the categories became the heading of a card which listed typical behaviors that might be expected to give information about that particular category. Each protocol was analyzed for each category independently to avoid as far as possible contamination by intercategory halo effects. Thus each interview protocol was analyzed nine times, each time with a different category function in mind. Further, no more than one interview of a given child was scored at any one time. As a result of this itemized scoring, we obtained not only a qualitative impression of the child's functioning (e.g., that he was an active child), but a quantitative expression of his functioning in terms of the number of explicit references to relevant behaviors made by the parent. We could, therefore, analyze the modes of functioning present in the behavior of the child on a quantitative basis.

It is important to note that for the purposes of scoring interview data one must be concerned only with the description of behavior as it appeared in the protocol. Every description of behavior was assumed to be true, and problems of the reliability and validity of the data were not the concern of the scorer. Only descriptions of actual behavior were scored, not interpretations of the behavior. This explicitness of procedure was essential, since the problem of scoring in relation to interpretation could develop not only with regard to the parents' statements, but also with regard to interpretations which could have been introduced by the scorers themselves.

The following is a definition of each category, with a description of specific behaviors which serve to illustrate some of the actual criteria utilized in the analysis of each behavior protocol.*

1]   Activity level

This category describes the extent to which a motor component exists in the child's functioning. In scoring, all data in the protocol concerned with motility were utilized. Some examples of representative behaviors that were scored as high activity are: "He moves a great deal in his sleep," "I can't leave him on the bed or couch because he always wriggles off," "He kicks and splashes so in the bath that I always have to mop up the floor afterward," "Dressing him becomes a battle, he squirms so," "He runs around so, that whenever we come in from the park I'm exhausted," "He

* Appendix I gives a number of illustrative behavioral items from various protocols which constitute scorable items for the three scale points for each of the nine categories. Appendix II gives the complete protocols of parental interviews from different children at ages three months, one year, and two years with the detailed scoring of the behavioral items.

crawls all over the house," and "Whenever I try to feed him he grabs for the spoon." Examples of low activity behaviors are: "In the bath he lies quietly and doesn't kick," "In the morning he's still in the same place he was when he fell asleep. I don't think he moves at all during the night," and "He can turn over, but he doesn't much."

2]   *Rhythmicity*

This category based itself upon the degree of rhythmicity or regularity of repetitive functions. Information concerning rest and activity, sleeping and waking, eating and appetite, and bowel and bladder function was utilized in the scoring.

A child's sleep-wake cycle was considered to be regular if the child fell asleep at approximately the same time each night and awoke at approximately the same time each morning. The child's functioning was considered to be irregular if there was a marked difference in the time of retiring and arising from day to day.

Information concerning the rest and activity periods of the child was derived from the protocol data on napping behavior. The child was scored as regular if he napped for the same length of time each day, and irregular if there was no discernible time pattern of function established.

Eating and appetite behavior was scored as regular if the protocol reported that the child demanded or accepted food readily at the same time each day and consumed approximately the same amount of food on corresponding diurnal occasions. The child was scored as irregular if his intake fluctuated widely from day to day, or if he could be induced to eat at times which differed widely from day to day.

Bowel function was scored as regular if the protocol indicated that the number and time of evacuations were constant from day to day, and irregular if the time and number were not readily predictable.

In all of these areas behavior was considered variable if there was evidence in the protocol that the child had established a pattern of functioning, but that there was some deviation from this pattern on occasion. This designation stands in contrast to a score of irregular, which denoted the failure to establish even a partial pattern.

3] *Approach or withdrawal*

This category describes the child's initial reaction to any new stimulus pattern, be it food, people, places, toys, or procedures. A few examples of initial approach responses are: "He always smiles at a stranger," "He loves new toys. He plays with one so much he often breaks it the first day," and "The first time he had his hair cut he sat on his father's lap and laughed through the whole thing." Withdrawal responses are illustrated by: "When I gave him his orange juice the first time he made a face. He didn't cry but he didn't suck it as eagerly as he does milk," "Whenever he sees a stranger he cries," "When we went to the doctor's for the first time he started to cry in the waiting room and didn't stop until we got home again," and "It takes him a long time to warm up to a new toy; he pushes it away and plays with something more familiar."

4] *Adaptability*

When considering adaptability, one is of necessity concerned with the sequential course of responses that are made to new or altered situations. In contrast to the previous category, it is not with the initial response that one is concerned. Rather, emphasis is on the ease or difficulty with which the initial pattern of response can be modified in socially desirable directions. Examples of adaptive behavior may be found in the following excerpts from parental interviews: "He used to spit out cereal whenever I gave it to him, but now he takes it fairly well, although still not as well as fruit," "Now when we go to the doctor's he doesn't start to cry till we undress him, and he even stops then if he can hold a toy," "At first he used to hold himself perfectly stiff in the bath, but now he kicks a little and pats the water with his hand," and "Every day for a week he'd go over to this stuffed lion someone gave him and say 'I don't like it,' but today he started playing with it and now you'd think it was his best friend."

Nonadaptive behavior can be illustrated by the following examples: "During the summer she used to nap in her carriage outside, and now that it's cold I've tried to put her in the crib, but she screams so I have to take her out and wheel her up and down the hall before she falls asleep," "Every time he sees the scissors he starts to scream and pull his hand away, so now I cut his nails when he's sleeping," "Whenever I put his snowsuit and hat on he screams and struggles, and he doesn't stop crying till we're outside," and "He doesn't like eggs and makes a face and turns his head away no matter how I cook them."

5] *Intensity of reaction*

In this category interest is in the energy content of the response, irrespective of its direction. A negative response may be as intense or as mild as a positive one. Scorable items for this category were provided by descriptions of behavior occurring in relation to stimuli, to preeliminations straining, to hunger, to repletion, to new foods, to attempts to control, to restraint, to diapering and dressing, to the bath, and to play and social contacts.

Examples of intense reactions are the following: "He cries whenever the sun shines in his eyes," "Whenever she hears music she begins to laugh and to jump up and down in time to it," "When he is hungry he starts to cry, and this builds up to a scream, and we can't distract him by holding or playing with him," "When she is full she spits the food out of her mouth and knocks the spoon away," "The first time we gave him cereal he spit it out and started to cry," "If we tell him 'No' he starts to cry," "Dressing is such a problem, he wriggles around so, and when I hold him so that he can't move he screams," and "She loves her bath so, that as soon as she hears the water running she tries to climb into the tub even if she's still fully dressed."

Examples of mild responses are: "He squints at a bright light but doesn't cry," "To a loud noise he jumps and startles a little, but he doesn't cry," "If he's hungry, he starts to whimper a bit, but if you play with him he won't really cry," "When she's had enough she turns her head away, and I know that it is time to stop," "If he does not like a new food he just holds it in his mouth without swallowing and then lets it drool out," "When we tell her 'No' she looks and smiles and then goes right on doing what she wants," "Now it's a pleasure to dress him, he stands up when you tell him to, and holds still when he has to," and "When other children take a toy away from him, he plays with something else, he doesn't try to get it back or cry."

6]   *Threshold of responsiveness*

This category refers to the intensity level of stimulation that is necessary to evoke a discernible response. The explicit form of response that occurs is irrelevant and may be of any quality, e.g., approaching or withdrawing, intense or mild. What is fundamental is the intensity of stimulus that had to be applied before a response of any kind could be elicited. The behaviors utilized were those concerning responses to sensory stimuli, environmental objects, and social contacts. We were also interested in the magnitude of difference between similar stimuli that had to obtain before the child showed evidences of discrimination.

Examples of the types of descriptions that were scored in this category are the following: "You can shine a bright light in his eyes and he doesn't even blink, but if a door closes he startles and looks up." This would be scored as high threshold for visual stimulation and low threshold for auditory stimuli. "I can never tell if he's wet except by feeling him, but if he has a bowel movement he fusses and is cranky until I change him." The statement indicates high threshold with respect to wet, but low threshold to the tactual complex associated with a bowel movement. "He loves fruit, but if I put even a little cereal in with it he won't eat it at all." This was scored as a low threshold response because it demonstrated the ability to discriminate small taste or textural differences. "He doesn't pay any attention to new people; he doesn't cry, but he doesn't really respond to them, either." This is an example of a high threshold in the area of social relations, as contrasted with "He laughs and smiles at a stranger, and starts to cry if they don't play with him," which was scored as low threshold. "He always cries when he sees a man wearing a hat even if it's his father," is illustrative of effective discrimination and was scored as a low threshold statement. "He makes himself at home anywhere, and runs around a strange house as if it were his," was scored as high threshold, while "He notices any little change. When we got new curtains for his room he spent a whole day crawling over to the window and pulling on them," received a low threshold score.

7] *Quality of mood*

This category describes the amount of pleasant, joyful, friendly behavior as contrasted with unpleasant, crying, unfriendly behavior. Consequently, statements which indicated crying behavior and unfriendly behavior were scored as negative mood statements, as in the following: "Whenever we put him to bed he cries for about five or ten minutes before falling asleep," "He cries at almost every stranger, and those that he doesn't cry at he hits," "I've tried to teach him not to knock down little girls and sit on them in the playground, so now he knocks them down and doesn't sit on them," and "Every time he sees food he doesn't like he starts to fuss and whine until I take it off the table." Examples of positive mood statements are: "Whenever he sees me begin to warm his bottle he begins to smile and coo," "He loves to look out of the window. He jumps up and down and laughs," "He always smiles at a stranger," and "If he's not laughing and smiling I know he's getting sick."

8] *Distractibility*

This category refers to the effectiveness of extraneous environmental stimuli in interfering with, or in altering the direction of, the ongoing behavior. If the course of a child who is crawling toward an electric light plug can be altered by presenting him with a toy truck, he would be considered distractible. If such efforts to alter his behavior are unsuccessful, he would be considered nondistractible. A child who is crying because he is hungry but stops when he is picked up is distractible, as opposed to the child who continues to cry until he is fed.

9] *Attention span and persistence*

This category refers to the definition of a direction of functioning and to the difficulty with which such an established direction of functioning can be altered. We were concerned with descriptions that gave information as to the attention span and the persistence of the child. By attention span is meant the length of time a particular activity was pursued. For example, if a two-year-old child could pour water from one cup to another for a half-hour, he would be scored as possessing a long attention span. If he engaged in this activity for five minutes, his attention span would be short. The attention span can be measured with regard to self-initiated activities, such as the above example of pouring water, as well as the child's participation in planned activities, such as listening to a story or listening to music. By persistence we mean the maintaining of an activity by a child in the face of obstacles to the continuation of the activity direction. Obstacles may be external. In the case of our child pouring water, if his mother comes along and says "No" and he continues to do it, he would be considered persistent. The obstacles may be much more directly related to the child's abilities. For example, the child who continually attempts to stand up although he always falls down would be scored as persistent, as would the child who struggles with a toy he can't make perform properly and not asking for help. The category, therefore, is an omnibus one which includes selectivity, persistence, and at a later age level frustration tolerance.

On the basis of these scoring approaches all eighty cases could be analyzed. It was possible to classify the children in accordance with their characteristic modes of functioning, and to determine the kinds of behavior that contributed the materials for analysis at each age level.

V

Problems of Reliability and Validity

TWO PROBLEMS must be dealt with before we proceed with the analysis of the data proper. Since the parents were the principal data source during the first two years of life, it is essential to determine the degree to which parental descriptions of behavior, as obtained by our interviewing technique, agree with descriptions of the child's behavior obtained by direct observations made by a trained observer. The first problem, therefore, is the validity of the data obtained from parental interview. It is clear that unless these data correspond with the data obtained through direct observation of the child's behavior, interperiod consistencies could represent constancy in the style of parental report rather than continuity in the child's mode of functioning. If, however, the information obtained by our interview technique did represent an accurate description of actual behavior, any interperiod stability in reactive characteristics could be interpreted as reflecting consistencies in the child's mode of functioning.

In order to determine the validity of parental report it was necessary to compare the scored interview protocol with a scored direct behavioral observation protocol for the same age period. To make such a comparison it was first necessary to determine the reliability of the scoring techniques used. If the technique of scoring were in itself unreliable, a failure to achieve agreement between the behavioral descriptions obtained by interview and those stemming from direct observation of the child could just as reasonably derive from scoring unreliability as from the nonvalidity of the interview descriptions. Conversely, if the scoring method were unreliable, agreement between the data of direct observation and of interview could be artifactual. Therefore, before dealing with the problem of validity, we must deal with the problem of reliability of the scoring.

A number of precautions were taken to maximize the objectivity of scoring the nine categories of reactivity. To begin with, each of the categories was clearly defined; the criteria were specified and illustrative examples provided. In addition, in order to minimize intercategory halo effects each protocol was analyzed for each category independently. These precautions, however, are in themselves no guarantee of reliability in scoring, but rather constitute standardized conditions of data analysis, the reliability of which must be determined.

The first step in testing the reliability of the scoring procedure was carried out by comparing the results obtained by two independent judges in the scoring of a series of twenty-two consecutively obtained cases. The children were characterized in terms of the preponderant behavior rating within each of the nine reaction patterns scored for each of the two judges' sets of scores. A high level of interscorer reliability was objectively demonstrated by the fact that these characterizations were identical in 90 percent of the 198 comparisons made. This high level of interscorer reliability was also achieved when a comparison was made of the results obtained by two additional scorers who were trained in this work at a later point in the study.

In addition to studying interscorer reliability, intrascorer reliability was examined. Interview protocols that had originally been scored by a trained scorer were submitted after three months to the same individual for rescoring without any identifying information. The rescore reliability of individual scorers was at as high a level as was interscorer reliability.

A third problem in the examination of scoring reliability derived from the nature of the categories of reactivity to which the described behaviors were scored. Even though these categories of reactivity were independently defined and scored for at different points in time, it is clear that they are not uncorrelated characteristics distributed orthogonally each to the other. Even on presumptive grounds one would expect such attributes as activity and intensity to be positively correlated. From the point of view of scorer reliability these possible intercorrelations are of no particular significance if one can demonstrate that, in fact, the scores for the different categories are independently arrived at and not contaminated by common contextual cues. In order to test this more directly each description of an individual behavior sequence present in the behavior protocols of nine different children was cut from context. Each snip description was mounted on a card and assigned a code number. These isolated bits, numbering 310 items, were scrambled together and each scored at different times for each of the nine categories by three data analysts working in isolation. Upon completion of the scoring of these snips, the fragments were reassembled and the snip scores compared with whole protocol scoring. No significant differences in score were obtained between whole and snip analysis of the data. As a consequence, it could be concluded that neither halo effects nor category intercorrelations contributed significantly to scoring reliability. In addition, the snip and whole protocol scorings for each of the three scorers achieved the previously noted level of agreement.

Having found that scoring reliability was high, we could now examine the problem of the validity of parental interview report on the children's behavior. In order to test the validity of parental behavioral description elicited by our interview technique, the characteristics of reactivity derived from scoring the interviews were compared with the scores derived from protocols of direct observation of the child's behavior by two independent trained observers. The reason for obtaining two independent observations was to permit an analysis of episodic behavioral variability as well as of the validity of parental description. It must be recognized that what is being compared in the validity assessment is behavior observed on a given day with parental descriptions that derive from observations and experiences collected by the parents over a three- to six-month period. As a result, any single observation period may deviate either from general behavioral course or from any other episodic observation. The use of independent observers making observations on different days permits an analysis of this problem.

Because of the age span encompassed in our behavioral analysis, it was considered necessary that the validating group include children representing the various age stages under consideration. Twenty-three children, ranging in age from less than three to eighteen months or more, were drawn from the study population by case number, and constituted the direct observation group. In eighteen of these cases observations were made by two observers, neither of whom was aware of the data obtained by parental interview. The direct observations were each independent of the other and were separated by seven to fourteen days. Each observation occurred within two weeks of an interview. In the remaining five cases only one observation was made within one week of the interview. The observation period was planned so that it would include a period of the day during which it would be possible to observe the child's behavior at feeding, sleeping, bathing, dressing, play, and elimination. Each observation lasted from two to three hours. Although no single period could be selected in which all phenomena were observable, the times chosen were ones in which most could be noted. In addition, the observers recorded the reactions of the children to themselves as strangers, both initially and throughout the course of the observation period. The observations were recorded as detailed behavioral descriptions.

The behavioral observations were scored by the same criteria as were the parent interviews, and preponderance for each reactive category determined. Clearly, two categories of reactivity—adaptability and rhythmicity—could not be assessed by a period of direct observation because they represented events occurring over longer time cycles. The validity of the remaining seven categories could be assessed from direct observational data. The direct observation scores were related to the parental interview scores derived from the interview closest in time to the observation. In addition, a comparison was made of each of the direct observation scores obtained by the two different observers at different points in time for the same child. The results of these comparisons indicated that the findings of each of the direct observations agreed with the parental interview assessment at the .01 level of confidence. The independent direct observations were in agreement with one another at the .05 level of confidence. Thus each of the episodes of observation produced behavior protocols which agreed more fully with the overall characterization of the child derived from the parental interview than they did with one another. This should not be surprising, since immediate circumstances present at each instant of episodic observation would be expected to enhance the difference between short periods more than they would affect the interrelation between any single period and overall functioning.

The assessment of reliability and validity permitted us to conclude that the data of the parent interview were a valid reflection of the child's behavior and that the methods of scoring were reliable and not significantly influenced either by scorer attitude or halo effect.

VI

Results

A LONGITUDINAL ANALYSIS of the first two years of life has been made of the behavioral characteristics of the eighty children in our sample who are now over two years of age. This analysis had two objectives:

1] To determine whether children are discriminably different in the patterning of behavioral reactivity in early infancy.

2] To analyze the degree to which features of behavioral reactivity identifiable in early infancy continue to characterize the child during his first two years.

At a first level of analysis the characteristics of the children were treated in terms of a preponderance model. In accordance with this model the child was classified at each age in terms of the most frequently occurring scale point at which his behaviors were judged to fall within each reactive category. The procedure followed may be seen by referring to Table 3, which shows the scoring record of a single child over the first five periods of study. In the first period, for the category rhythmicity, the child had seven instances in which his behavior was judged as regular, two instances in which he was judged to be variable, and four instances in which his behavior was judged to be irregular. In terms of a preponderance model, such a child would be rated as regular. Similarly, a score of sixteen for adaptive, two for variable, and five for nonadaptive resulted in a classification of the child as adaptive for the preponderance model. Therefore, during the first period of his

TABLE 3

AN EXAMPLE OF THE LONGITUDINAL RECORD OF A SINGLE CHILD
INDICATING THE TOTAL NUMBER OF SCORED ITEMS IN EACH BEHAVIOR
RATING FOR THE FIVE AGE PERIOD SUBDIVISIONS

Age Span (Mos.)	Activity			Rhythmicity			Adaptability			Approach			Threshold			Intensity			Mood			Distractibility			Persistence			Total
	H	M	L	R	V	I	A	V	N	A	V	W	H	M	L	I	V	M	+	V	−	Y	V	N	Y	V	N	
I 0-6	5	3	0	7	2	4	16	2	5	4	0	5	3	7	5	3	1	13	7	0	13	2	0	0	2	0	0	109
II 6-11	2	1	1	4	0	2	7	0	5	1	0	4	3	3	4	3	0	4	4	0	7	1	0	0	1	0	2	59
III 11-17	0	2	1	3	1	2	5	0	4	4	0	0	3	5	0	2	0	6	4	0	5	1	0	1	0	0	2	51
IV 18-22	2	1	0	3	2	2	10	0	8	5	0	0	1	4	5	6	0	6	8	0	6	5	0	0	2	0	2	78
V 22-27	3	0	1	5	2	0	11	2	1	1	0	0	1	4	3	3	0	8	8	0	3	1	0	0	0	0	2	59

life, the child whose record is illustrated in Table 3 was characterized as highly active, regular, adaptive, withdrawing, moderate in his threshold, mild in his reaction, negative in mood, distractible, and persistent.

When all the children were scored for their first period characteristics in terms of a preponderance model, varying distributions resulted for each of the nine characteristics of reactivity. As may be seen in Table 4, the group of children as a whole had model characteristics of high activity, regularity, adaptability, approach, low threshold, mild reactiveness, positive mood, ready distractibility, and persistence. The distributions for each of the primary reactive characteristics tended to be skewed as the result of using only the modal score as the basis for categorizing the individual for the primary reactive characteristic under consideration. However, even when so demanding a model is used, individual differences among children are demonstrable, particularly for such characteristics as activity level, threshold, intensity of reaction, mood, and distractibility.

The stability of the nine primary reaction characteristics may also be explored within the framework of the preponderance

TABLE 4

DISTRIBUTION OF THE NUMBER OF CHILDREN IN PERIOD I WITH
PREPONDERANT SCORES IN EACH OF THE RATINGS IN THE NINE
CATEGORIES. THE TOTAL NUMBER OF CHILDREN OBSERVED IS EIGHTY

Activity		Rhythmicity		Adaptability	
high	35	regular	65	adaptive	70
moderate	28	variable	2	variable	0
low	7	irregular	9	nonadaptive	8
total	70*		76		78

Approach		Threshold		Intensity	
approach	66	high	13	intense	18
variable	0	moderate	17	variable	0
withdrawal	11	low	46	mild	57
total	77		76		75

Mood		Distractibility		Persistence	
positive	55	yes	51	yes	64
variable	0	variable	0	variable	1
negative	17	no	17	no	5
total	72		68		70

* A number of children's scores were evenly divided between two or more of the ratings in a category. These "ties" are not included in the table.

model. Two approaches have been used: 1] the interperiod frequency of the preponderant rating for each category during the first two years of life; and 2] the frequency of agreement between the preponderant ratings in any two periods, such as I and V, where these are viewed as initial and terminal periods of a predictive study.

The stability of preponderance ratings for each of the eighty children in all nine categories as a group for the first two years of life was first determined. Chi-square analysis of the interperiod agreement was statistically significant beyond the .01 level in each child. The occurrence of stability of preponderances for all five periods, for four out of five, three out of five, and two out of five periods, was then compared with the frequency that would be expected on the basis of chance alone. The calculation was based on 720 instances—eighty children in each of nine categories. The results of this analysis are expressed in Figure 1 and indicate that

FIGURE 1

The percent of longitudinal comparisons in which varying levels of stability did occur and would be expected to occur on the basis of chance variations. Stability was gauged by the largest number of periods in which any particular behavioral rating reappears as the preponderant one in the five periods of observation.

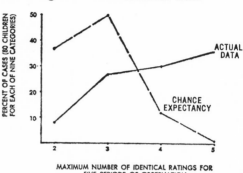

MAXIMUM NUMBER OF IDENTICAL RATINGS FOR
FIVE PERIODS OF OBSERVATION

the actual findings are in an opposite direction to a chance distribution. In 35.8 percent of the 720 instances identical preponderant ratings were found in all five periods, while chance alone would have given a 1.2 percent outcome. At the other extreme, preponderance stability in only two out of five periods occurred in only 8.2 percent of the cases, while chance alone would have given a 37 percent score. Finally, the percentage of stability of preponderance ratings of each of the nine categories separately, for four out of five and three out of five periods, and the comparison with chance expectancy was determined. The results of this analysis are expressed in Figure 2 and indicate that the stability of preponderance ratings for the first two years of life for the eighty children was significantly greater than chance expectancy for each of the nine categories.

The finding of stability of preponderance ratings is confirmed by the results of a predictive analysis. For each child the prediction was made that the same scale point would be the preponderant one in the initial (I) and terminal period (V) of analysis. The results of this predictive analysis are summarized in Table 5. The total number of predictions made in each, category does not equal eighty because of the elimination of those instances in which a tied preponderance occurred in either period I or V. As indicated

FIGURE 2

Percent of cases in which the preponderant rating in each category remained the same in at
least (A) four of the five periods or (B) three of the five periods of observation from birth to
approximately two years. Chance expectation is also indicated for each level of stability.

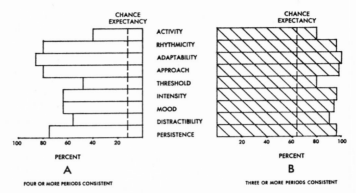

A
FOUR OR MORE PERIODS CONSISTENT

B
THREE OR MORE PERIODS CONSISTENT

in Table 5, the agreement of preponderance ratings of periods I
and V occurred with sufficient frequency in eight out of the nine
categories to support the predictions at better than the .001 level

TABLE 5

PREDICTIONS OF LIKE PREPONDERANCE RATINGS
IN AGE PERIODS I AND V

Reactive Category	Total	Confirmed	Inaccurate	Binomial Test
Activity	62	24	38	0.8**
Rhythmicity	71	49	22	6.2*
Adaptability	75	66	9	9.9*
Approach	67	50	17	6.1*
Threshold	72	42	30	4.4*
Intensity	73	50	23	6.3*
Mood	67	44	23	5.6*
Distractibility	61	45	16	6.5*
Persistence	63	51	12	8.0*

* Significantly different from chance beyond 0.001 level.
** Not statistically significant.

of confidence. The one prediction not supported involved activity
level. More detailed examination of the age-to-age data for the
activity level category showed that the shift responsible for the lack

of predictive success occurred between periods IV and V. As indicated in Table 6, when the preponderance ratings for this category between periods I and IV are compared, the predictive accuracy

TABLE 6

PREDICTIVE STABILITY WITHIN ACTIVITY CATEGORY, CONTRASTING PERIODS IV AND V AS "TERMINAL" PERIODS

Prediction from Period to Period	Total	Confirmed	Inaccurate	Binomial Test
I and V	62	24	38	0.8**
I and IV	56	36	20	4.8*
II and V	60	23	37	0.7**

* Significantly different from chance beyond 0.001 level.
** Not statistically significant.

is significant at the .001 level, while the comparison between periods II and V, a similar age span, shows a predictive accuracy only at the chance level. An analysis of age period preponderance ratings beyond two years, now in progress, will be required to determine whether this shift in activity level is a transient or persistent phenomenon.

Within the framework of the preponderant ratings as a means of characterizing the children, another issue may be pursued. A possibility that must be considered is that the age-to-age consistency of ratings, previously demonstrated, may be a function of the overriding behavioral similarity of all the children reported in this study. It may not be features of behavioral individuality that remain stable, but general attributes of behavior may persist throughout the age span covered. If nearly all the children in our sample are preponderantly regular, then demonstrations of longitudinal stability or predictive accuracy may be little more than a reflection of the insensitivity of the measures used and would be similar to the correct prediction of hot weather in the Sahara. This issue may be explored by several routes. Table 4, previously presented, reveals that the distributions of preponderant ratings in many behavior categories are, in fact, heavily concentrated in one of the three respective scale positions. The question then remains: Is longitudinal stability only likely to be found in the most prevalent preponderant rating in each behavior category? If this is the case, then the usefulness of the preponderant ratings as a general method of characterizing the children would be seriously limited. However, if in each category the least frequently occurring preponderant ratings in the initial period also remain stable, no contraindications remain. The children whose particular preponderant rating was least representative of the whole sample of eighty children were selected for each of the nine behavior categories. The only restriction imposed was that the group in each category should include at least five children. As may be seen from Table 4, the low scale point in activity appears as the preponderant initial rating only seven times, as compared with 35 and 28 for the high and moderate ratings, respectively. In rhythmicity, nine children were essentially irregular, while 65 were regular.

Similarly, the number of amodal individuals may be identified for each of the remaining categories of primary reactivity. When the stability over the five periods of these amodal individuals is explored (Table 7), it is found that their preponderance ratings for six of the nine categories of reactivity are markedly

TABLE 7

DISTRIBUTION OF CASES IN WHICH THE LESS PREVALENT INITIAL
PREPONDERANT RATINGS IN EACH CATEGORY REMAINED STABLE
FROM BIRTH TO TWO YEARS OF AGE

Behavior Category and Preponderant Rating	Number of Children	CASES IN WHICH THE INITIAL AND STABLE PREPONDERANT RATING REMAINED THE SAME.	
		Number	Percent
Low Activity	7	1	14.3
Irregular	9	1	11.0
Nonadaptive	8	1	12.5
Withdrawal	11	3	27.3
High Threshold	13	9	69.2
Intense	18	14	77.7
Negative Mood	17	9	52.9
Nondistractible	17	11	64.7
Nonpersistent	5	2	40.
Total	105	51	

stable over time. Thus the amodal individuals appeared to be equally stable as the more typically functioning members of the sample. It may therefore be concluded that the stabilities found by the use of the preponderance model are not merely the function of the insensitivity of the method of measurement. Rather they reflect the stability of behavioral functioning of the children under study. This conclusion is strengthened by the fact that 50 percent of the amodal individuals on an overall basis maintained their stabilities, while for intensity and threshold 77.7 percent and 69.2 percent of the children respectively had stable preponderant ratings.

Despite the usefulness of the preponderance model for the identification of individuality and its persistence, it has two apparent limitations which must be overcome if more detailed quantitative analysis of individual differences in behavioral reactivity is to take place. In the first instance, the preponderance model utilizes only that fraction of the available data that is most frequent in its occurrence and eliminates from consideration the nonpreponderant responses. This procedure has the marked virtue of characterizing each individual in terms of his most typical way of behaving. However, two children are scored as active by this model when one has sixteen high activity, no variable, and one low activity ratings, whereas the other child has nine high activity, two variable, and eight low activity ratings. Although both children are individuals who preponderantly exhibit high activity level, their differences as expressed in the distribution of their total scores in the other activity categories must be considered if they are to be most fully differentiated from each other in a quantitative sense.

The second apparent limitation of the preponderance model is to be found in the markedly skewed distributions for several of the nine categories of primary reactivity. The fact of skewed distributions for certain of the nine categories of reactivity may be viewed in two ways. One interpretation is that the preponderance model is too insensitive and therefore results in artifactual homogenization. Another, and probably more correct interpretation, is that in a qualitative sense the behavioral reactivity of most children is similar, and that the preponderance model accurately distinguishes the qualitatively modal from the qualitatively amodal individuals.

To incorporate all of the data available, i.e., preponderant as well as nonpreponderant scorings, two additional models for data analysis were used. The first of these was a ranks model, and the second a percent-rank index.

In the ranks model the child is characterized at each age or period of observation by the relative number of items scored in each scale point within each category of behavior. For each age the preponderant rating is assigned rank one, the least frequently occurring is assigned rank three, and the one with the intermediate frequency is assigned rank two. In this manner the characterization of each child at any age period is determined by the hierarchical order of the relative number of items scored in each scale point within each of the nine categories.

The scores for the child used in Table 3 are recast as ranks in Table 8. In Table 9 the distributions of children who achieved different rank in the nine categories are presented. As may be seen, a ranks model provides a much less skewed distribution than a preponderance model. It also makes possible the application of the Friedman Two-Way Analysis of Variance technique for the calculation of the stability of rank patterns. While for each category the percentage of cases with interperiod stability would be 5 percent on the basis of chance expectancy, the actual percentage of cases exhibiting interperiod stability over the first two years is considerably higher. The obtained percentages, as may be seen in Table 10, range from 27.5 percent for activity to 92.5 percent for mood. In each case tallied, the likelihood that the consistency of the particular ranks or hierarchies of scores recorded in the five periods could be attributable to chance variation was less than .05.

The ranks model for the characterization of behavior provides an additional basis for the examination of longitudinal stability. Rather than relying solely on the preponderant scores, the analysis of these data takes into account the interperiod consistency of the relative number of items scored in each scale point. The absence of individual longitudinal stability is revealed by

TABLE 8

AN EXAMPLE OF A LONGITUDINAL RECORD OF A SINGLE CHILD, INCLUDING THE RANK ORDER OF THE RELATIVE NUMBER OF SCORED ITEMS IN EACH BEHAVIOR RATING FOR THE FIVE AGE PERIOD SUBDIVISIONS. THE DATA OF TABLE 3 ARE RECAST HERE AS RANKS.

Age Span	Activity			Rhythmicity			Adaptability			Approach			Threshold			Intensity			Mood			Distractibility			Persistence		
	H	M	L	R	V	I	A	V	N	A	V	W	H	M	L	I	V	M	+	V	−	Y	V	N	Y	V	N
I 0–6	1	2	3	1	3	2	1	3	2	2	3	1	3	1	2	2	3	1	2	3	1	1	2.5	2.5	2.5	2.5	1
II 6–11	1	2.5	2.5	1	3	2	1	3	2	2	3	1	2.5	2.5	1	2	3	1	2	3	1	2.5	2.5	1	2.5	2.5	1
III 11–17	3	1	2	1	3	2	1	3	2	1	2.5	2.5	2	1	3	2	3	1	2	3	1	3	1.5	1.5	2.5	3	1.5
IV 18–22	1	2	3	1	2.5	2.5	1	3	2	1	2.5	2.5	3	2	1	1.5	3	1.5	1	3	2	1	2.5	2.5	2.5	1.5	3
V 22–27	1	3	2	1	2	3	1	2	3	1	2.5	2.5	3	1	2	2	3	1	1	3	2	1	2.5	2.5	2.5	2.5	1

TABLE 9

INDIVIDUAL CHILDREN'S RANK ORDER OF SCALE POSITIONS BASED ON THE RELATIVE NUMBER OF SCORED ITEMS IN EACH RATING IN PERIOD I

Behavior Category and Rating Scale	1-2-3	1-3-2	2-1-3	3-1-2	3-2-1	2-3-1	1-2.5-2.5	2.5-1-2.5	2.5-2.5-1	Other
Activity high—moderate—low	10	11	6	11	0	2	14	11	5	10
Rhythmicity regular—variable—irregular	26	27	1	0	2	5	12	1	2	4
Adaptability adaptive—variable—nonadaptive	11	48	0	0	0	7	11	0	1	2
Approach approach—variable—withdrawal	5	49	0	0	0	9	12	0	2	3
Threshold high—moderate—low	1	11	5	10	14	23	1	2	9	4
Intensity intense—variable—mild	1	15	0	0	4	52	2	0	1	5
Mood positive—variable—negative	0	42	0	0	0	15	13	0	2	8
Distractibility yes—variable—no	4	6	0	0	0	5	41	0	12	12
Persistence yes—variable—no	3	7	1	0	0	0	54	0	5	10

Distribution of children in each category with particular rank order of occurrence of behavior items among the respective ratings. The rating with the greatest number of items in a particular period is assigned rank 1, etc. The order of rating on the behavior scale is enumerated in column one. Thus rank 1-3-2 in activity indicates that for this child most of the scored items in activity were high with the smallest number falling on moderate.

66

TABLE 10

RESULTS OF FRIEDMAN TWO-WAY ANALYSIS OF VARIANCE

Category	Percent of Cases with Interperiod Stability
Activity	27.5
Rhythmicity	65.0
Adaptability	83.8
Approach	81.2
Threshold	41.2
Intensity	87.5
Mood	92.5
Distractibility	36.2
Persistence	65.0

random alteration in the relative number of behavioral items scored in each behavior rating over the series of age periods. That is, in the longitudinal record of each child (as presented in Table 8) each rating in a behavior category, such as high, moderate, and low activity, should appear equally often as the preponderant rating, rank one, as the second most prevalent score, rank two, and as the least frequently occurring, rank three. However, longitudinal stability is in fact predominant. Analysis of the data reveals that the particular hierarchical order of scored items characterizing a child tends to persist relatively unchanged in a significantly large number of children.

Further examination of Table 10 suggests that the pattern of scores in each category may reveal features of individuality of the children, as well as characteristics of the behavioral attributes under examination. To begin with, the analysis of the persistence of the hierarchical pattern of scores in each category reveals some variation among the nine behavior categories. For example, 74 of the 80 children studied (92.5 percent), maintained a consistent pattern of responses in mood, 65 percent in rhythmicity, and 27.5 percent in activity. The variation among categories may be attributable to the developmental characteristics of the particular aspects of behavior included in each response category. Perhaps mood exhibits one particular developmental trend, activity another, and so on. However, this factor is apparently compounded with some additional source of individuality of the children; there is also variation in the number of categories each child maintained with a reliable, recurrent order. On the average, the number of rank patterns maintained consistently was 5.8. Therefore, almost two thirds of the nine categories were sustained by each child. However, as indicated in Table 11, one child maintained consist-

TABLE 11

CONSISTENCY OF RANK PATTERN IN PERIODS I–V

Total Number of Consistent Categories	Number of Children
9	1
8	9
7	13
6	23
5	21
4	11
3	1
2	1
44	80

ency in all nine categories, nine children in eight of the categories, etc. All in all, 78 of the 80 children maintained a statistically reliable rank pattern over the first two years in four or more of the nine categories. Thus part of the overall variation in the regularity of recurrence of the order of scored items may be a function of the behavior characteristics involved, but part may be dependent on characteristics of individuality of the children. The latter may be a function of both intrinsic and environmental factors that need further elaboration.

As may be seen by a comparison of the manner in which our sample of children was distributed by use of the preponderance model and the distributions which were derived from the ranks model, the use of a ranking procedure increased the range of variation in the sample and made possible a more detailed consideration of individual differences in behavioral functioning. However, even the ranks model results in a considerable degree of residual skewness. In order to magnify still further individual differences and to increase the spread of our distributions within each category, a third model, which we have called the percent-rank index, was used. In the percent-rank index model the children are characterized in terms of the relative degree to which they exhibit a particular aspect of any of the nine categories of primary reactivity. The child's score for any characteristic of reactivity, therefore, represents the ratio of the number of occasions on which his behavior has been rated to fall at one of the three scoring positions to the total number of behaviors that were scored for this reactive category. If in a given child a total of twenty behaviors were distributed at all three points in the activity category, and four of these behaviors were rated as low activity, then the percent index score for low activity would be $\frac{4}{20} \times 100$ percent index score. The children are next ranked in the order of the magnitude of these percent index scores. This procedure for the eighty cases resulted in a series of ranks from one to eighty. The child's percent-rank index score represented his position in this ranking sequence. Obviously, such a rank index score could be computed for any score position for any category of reactivity. However, since we wished to magnify differences between children, the particular rating position chosen for each category was that polar extreme which appeared least frequently in the sample as a whole as the preponderant or modal rating during the first two years of life. This resulted in the set of selections indicated in Table 12.

As may be seen from Figure 3, the use of a percent index

TABLE 12

Category	Amodal Point
Activity	Low
Rhythmicity	Irregular
Adaptability	Nonadaptive
Approach	Withdrawal
Threshold	High
Intensity	Intense
Mood	Negative
Distractibility	No
Persistence	No

FIGURE 3

Distribution of the number of children in Period I with the percent ratings in each of the categories.

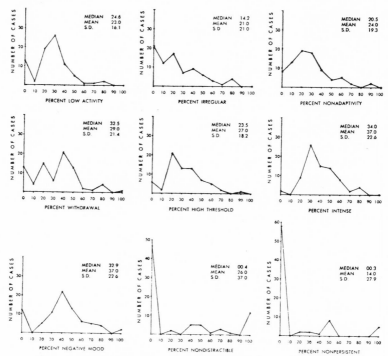

score resulted in a considerable increment in the spread of our distributions for each reactive category. Although a J-shaped curve resulted from such analysis of the category of rhythmicity, and markedly skewed distributions remained for the categories of distractibility and persistence, the remaining six categories came to be distributed in a relatively normal manner when the percent-rank index model was used.

Using the percent-rank index findings, we sought to determine the persistence of individual differences in reactivity over the period of the first two years of life. In order to treat the data longitudinally, rank order correlations were calculated among all combinations of the five periods into which the two-year span was divided. These rank order correlations are presented in Table 13. Because of complications resulting from the frequency of occurrence of tied ranks, two of the reactive categories, distractibility and persistence, could not meaningfully be examined by correlational techniques. The remaining seven categories of reactivity, however, could be subjected to correlational analysis. As may be seen from Table 13, this analysis resulted in seventy interperiod correlations representing all interperiod combinations. Of these correlations forty-five of the seventy were statistically significant at less than the .05 level of confidence. Thirty-eight of the forty-five statistically significant correlations were of sufficient size to be significant at less than the .01 level of confidence. The likelihood of this number of significant correlations occurring by chance is less than one in a thousand.

As is clear from the table, the treatment of interperiod relations resulted in ten correlation coefficients for each period of reactivity. For four of these categories—rhythmicity, adaptability, threshold, and intensity—seven or more of the ten interperiod comparisons resulted in significant levels of positive correlation. For the remaining categories the findings were six significant positive intercorrelations for mood, five for activity, and three for approach. The most striking stability was found for intensity, for which category all ten of the intercorrelations resulted in coefficients significant at less than the 01 level of confidence.

In summary, each of the three methods of data analysis—preponderance, rank, and percent-rank index—has contributed evidence that initially identifiable characteristics of reactivity are persistent features of the child's behavior throughout the first two years of life.

TABLE 13

RANK ORDER CORRELATIONS

Interperiod Correlations for the Five Age Periods of the First Two Years of Life. In Each Category and Each Interperiod Comparison Rho Is Based on the Percent of Rank Order Data.

Periods	Activity	Rhythmicity	Adaptability	Approach	Threshold	Intensity	Mood
1–2	.37**	.53**	.58**	.37**	.50**	.45**	.66**
1–3	.24*	.12	.44**	.36**	.38**	.41**	.58**
1–4	−.09	.23*	.32**	−.02	.30**	.38**	.31**
1–5	−.15	.23*	.21	.04	.00	.30**	.05
2–3	.56**	.38**	.51**	.23*	.67**	.45**	.60**
2–4	.15	.14	.23*	.16	.29**	.36**	.32**
2–5	.13	.23*	.07	.16	.16	.40**	.01
3–4	.39**	.39**	.40**	.02	.37**	.49**	.29**
3–5	.14	.26*	.10	.00	.20	.40**	.02
4–5	.42**	.16	.28**	.11	.29**	.28**	.20

* Significant beyond the .05 level of confidence.
** Significant beyond the .01 level of confidence.

VII

Theoretical Implications

ALTHOUGH THERE is always a great temptation in the discussion of theoretical problems to become diffuse and to seek to embrace an increasingly broad area of conceptualization, the present discussion will be restricted to those issues which are directly relevant to the question of psychological individuality. Historically, two principal directions have been explored in order to identify sources for individual differences in psychological organization. The first has been a typologic view which, from the time of Hippocrates [1] to the contemporary work of Sheldon,[2,3] has sought to find the primary basis for individual differences in some physical or physiologic characteristic of the person. The second view, from John Locke [4] to Sigmund Freud,[5] has assumed individuality to be the product of circumstances in developmental experience and so to be a reactive phenomenon.

From an overall theoretic standpoint each of these well-established directions of inquiry has an internal consistency of scientific attitude and fundamental assumption despite differences in detail. The fact that Hippocrates and Galen sought to characterize people in humoral terms, and Sheldon to differentiate among them on the basis of bodily proportions, or that Locke was primarily concerned with cognitive experience, and Freud with motivational and affective learning, represents differences in detail and emphasis rather than in principle. The findings of the present study make it possible for us to consider these systematic approaches to individual differences from a new perspective.

The typologic and the reactive developmental positions may be viewed as complementary rather than as antagonistic. If one considers the aspects of functioning with which each has been concerned, it becomes clear that typology has focused its interest on problems of temperament, whereas reactive theories have dealt with adaptive organizations of the personality. It is of interest that, when confronted with temperamental questions, reactive theory, as illustrated in Freud, tends to fall back upon constitutionalism and inborn difference in energy level. Conversely, typologies use reactive conceptualizations in order to account for motive and adaptation.

Moreover, both theoretical positions share the tendency to relegate behavior to a subordinate position in their consideration of basic psychological functions. Reactive theorists, as exemplified by contemporary psychoanalysis, direct their emphasis to the presumed antecedents and consequences of the behavior rather than to the behavior itself. Lois Murphy clearly illustrates this tendency in her description of thumbsucking in two babies. She writes that "when Baby A sucks her thumb nothing will deter her, while Baby B gives it up quite easily when it is removed from his mouth; his sucking drive is not as strong as Baby A's." [6] In this description there is a direct movement from a behavioral fact to a presumed motivational antecedent. An alternative approach, in which a behavioral focus is primary, would lead, not to an immediate exploration of motive or other presumed antecedent, but to a more general consideration of a broader body of behavioral information. One would be led to inquire whether the intensity of responses in Baby A is generally greater than in Baby B, and whether, in a variety of behavioral situations, Baby A exhibits a degree of persistence and nondistractibility markedly greater than Baby B. If both such questions are answered in the affirmative, then the behavioral characteristics, the antecedents of which one needs to identify, are not a sucking drive or orality, but persistence, intensity, and nondistractibility. A primary attachment to behavioral analysis therefore leads to the consideration of the index behavior, i.e., the thumbsucking, in its relation to the more general patterning of behavioral function. A view in which attention is immediately directed toward antecedents for each behavioral datum leads to a restrictive concern with isolated phenomena. Different behaviors are related at the interpretive, but not at the behavioral, level. Obviously, a failure to be concerned with the behavioral setting of any index behavior poses quite different problems for the study of underlying mechanisms, antecedents, and processes than does a behaviorally oriented approach. Where Murphy needs to explain persistence in sucking per se—by postulating a special drive—a fuller behavioral analysis leads to the need for obtaining an understanding of the mechanisms for intensity of reaction, persistence, and nondistractibility.

The typologic position is epitomized in the work of Sheldon and Stevens,[3] who have attempted to relate characteristics of physical growth and form to aspects of temperament. Starting out with three types of physical organization—endomorphy, mesomorphy, and ectomorphy—they have obtained correlations of the order of .80 between the body type and such temperamental generalizations as viscerotonia, somatotonia, and cerebrotonia. A serious criticism has been raised on methodologic grounds, since the psychologists who rated the subjects for temperamental characteristics were fully familiar with the physical typology and its presumed implications. Despite the authors' claim that great care was taken to avoid it, the probability is high that contamination contributed to the reported correlations. A second criticism may be advanced on theoretical grounds. The typologic position implies that the temperamental characteristics are the direct consequence of the physical traits. No serious consideration is given to the possibility that given body types selectively predispose to differential environmental involvements, which in themselves may be sufficient to account for the levels of intercorrelation between body types and temperament found in other more carefully controlled studies.[7,8] The simplistic typologic position fails to examine the behavioral consequences of given body types and assumes that the body type as such may be causally related to certain temperamental generalities.

Although both reactive and typologic theories have been used to explain individuality of psychological functioning, there is little doubt that reactive theory has been the more influential position. Despite continued lip service to the view that organismic characteristics exert a significant influence on the direction of individual development, attention for almost half a century has in the main been concentrated on the study of psychodynamic and environmental influences as sources for individual difference.

There can be little doubt that such emphasis has resulted in an increased understanding of the roles which motivational factors and styles of parent-child interaction play in individual development. However, what began as an emphasis on a previously neglected aspect of the developmental process has in fact come to be identified by many workers [9,10,11] with the entirety of processes contributing to psychological individuality. This tendency to identify the part with the whole is recognized in the precautionary suggestion of Bruch [12] that the placing of prime and even sole responsibility on parents and their practices for either the satisfactory or pathologic development of their offspring may be a destructive myth productive of both needless anxiety and confusion as well as baseless aspirations.

The rejection of psychodynamic concepts in development and the emphasizing of behavioral analysis do not involve a retreat to nosology. A mere recital of the phenomenal facts of behavior is insufficient for understanding its course, mechanisms, and consequences, and any acceptable theory must go beyond mere descriptive taxonomy. However, without a detailed analysis of behavior there can be no clear identification of the facts that require explanation.

The contrast between psychodynamic explanatory efforts and the classificatory emphasis dominant in earlier psychiatric systems contributed in no small part to the widespread attractiveness of psychoanalysis as a psychological system. In place of taxonomy, psychoanalysis sought to account for individual behavior in terms of process reflected in a triad of relationships. Each behavior was viewed as having both a goal-object and a pattern of tactics used in connection with the goal. These tactics assumed *1]* a method for obtaining the goal; *2]* a method for inhibiting goal-directed behavior; and 3] methods for resolving conflicts between mutually exclusive goals. Within this framework a classical analysis of behavior from the psychodynamic standpoint had to include the identification both of the drive and the object to which it was attached—drive state and drive object—and the tactic elaborated in the drive-environment relationship.

Analyses of psychological characteristics in infants and young children within the psychoanalytic framework have represented an application of these principles. Early behaviors have tended to be explained in terms of the dynamics of drive states and their environmental relations. From a research point of view the attachment to the psychoanalytic position has not been without difficulty. Since the entire theory rests upon the obtaining of data for the analysis of psychological functions through verbalized introspections, acts well beyond the skills of infants and young children, the identification of initial characteristics of psychological individuality has not been possible in psychoanalytic terms. As indicated earlier, Spitz,[13] recognizing this difficulty, has lamented the need to study behavior in young children rather than intrapsychic states, which are inaccessible because psychoanalytic introspection is inapplicable as an investigative method in young children prior to elaborate language development. Bowlby [14,15] has attempted to extend the concept of motivation to embrace broad ethologic manifestations which he interprets as biologic interpersonal motives and, further, has sought to include such relations in the category of psychodynamics. Thus at several levels, even within the psychoanalytic movement, the adequacy and applicability of drive object, achievement-tactic analyses of child development, and particularly of infant behavioral patterns, has been seriously questioned.

Several workers have pursued the logic of the nonrelatedness of psychoanalytic method to the analysis of infant behavior even further. Escalona,[16,17] recognizing the untestability at this age level of psychoanalytic propositions, has substituted concepts of threshold, behavioral intensity, and arousal state for unusable psychodynamic formulations. However, she has continued to use psychoanalytic conceptualizations as the framework into which these nonpsychoanalytic data are assimilated. Richmond,[18] in a similar way, has in fact studied autonomic physiology, while on a theoretical level he has discussed psychoanalytic motivational concepts.

In the study of the older child, psychoanalytic theory has led to a search for the sources of a variety of psychopathological phenomena in underlying purposes, motives, and conceptualizable goals and aims. The search has tended to include the assumption that such motives must exist for all behavior. In other words, the unwarranted extension is made that a pattern of behavior could not occur unless the individual possessed a purpose and aim, either conscious or unconscious, which could produce it. This assumption is encouraged by the very nature of psychodynamic formulations, such as repression, reaction formation, and sublimation. Such concepts make it possible to "explain" any aspect of overt behavior as due to some postulated unconscious motive, whether the behavior corresponds to or is opposite to the motive.

A recent discussion serves to illustrate certain varieties of difficulty in research when one adheres to psychodynamic interpretation. A predictive failure in one study [19] of child development was converted into a predictive success through the use of *ad hoc* reasoning characterized by postdictive interpretations. An initial assumption was made that the mother's "own reaction formation toward dirt and messiness would result in attempts at early toilet training, and in her adopting an overstrict attitude, which would produce similar tendencies in the child." This prediction was not supported by the mother's behavior. She did not initiate consistent or early toilet training; in fact, training was both inconsistent and late. In order to account for this unpredicted behavior, an elaborate argument was advanced. The author stated:

But the conflict inherent in toilet training—and this conflict is a ubiquitous one—did not lead, as was assumed, to an intensification of this mother's defensive processes, but rather to a breakthrough or indulgence of her original impulses, in that they were given free reign in the child. One wonders whether similar circumstances may not be involved in the frequently encountered inconsistencies in toilet training. It seems that the direct contact with the anal activity of the child —the seduction thus coming from the child—stimulates the mother's own old conflicts and induces her at times to relinquish her role as mother. Temporarily, she can thus gratify her old pleasure in uncontrolled soiling through identification with the child.

It is clear from this structuring of the argument that any course the mother adopted would have served, via *ad hoc* extensions, to support the original hypothesis in spite of predictive failure.

Another research difficulty in psychodynamic interpretation involves the use of fragmented analogy for interpreting individual differences. In this method certain features of phenomenal similarity between behavior in young children and later patterns of more complex functioning are exploited to yield assumed identities in underlying motive. An excellent example may be found in Benjamin's discussion of doll play.[20] He used the infant's retention or expulsion of toys as an indicator of a general tendency toward outward or inward direction of functioning. Later social behavior was then presumed to be a direct reflection of this same directional tendency. In a more general way, Murphy,[6] basing herself on Levy,[21] has identified vigor and persistence of sucking in the newborn infant with a general underlying property of oral drive, which is then presumably channeled into more complex manifestations of orality as the child develops. These predictions go beyond correlation and involve the assumption that features of interpretation used to characterize the infant are continuously present and merely manifest themselves in different forms at different ages.

The instances chosen are not atypical illustrations of the general propensity of psychoanalytic theory to assume constancy of drive characteristics at different ages. Investigations based on this view have not studied the child longitudinally in order to determine the sequence of interactions and transformations that constitutes the process of development from the time of initial behavior to eventual outcome. The exercises in prediction have been largely presumptive and based upon the relation of one theory to another. It is important to note that the method has not been based upon the conviction of the validity of a firmly established theory of developmental process. The predictive indices have been *ad hoc,* or fragmented analogies between interpretations of earlier behavioral observations and later presumed or inferred interpretations of intrapsychic organizations.

In contrast to the psychodynamic approach to sources for individuality, the present study has directed its attention to the actual characteristics of the individual child as these have been revealed in his behavior. In contrast to the approach of Murphy, in which sucking behavior is used as an indicator of hypothesized oral drive, we have used the same behaviors as indicators of the child's intensity of reacting, of the persistence he exhibits in his functioning, and, under certain circumstances, of relative nondistractibility. This type of analysis does not involve the necessity for postulating drives and drive states. Instead, a given behavior provides a datum for one or more general behavioral categories. Thus, behaviors are linked one to the other not by assumed drives, but by common properties of reactivity—that is, styles of functioning, As a consequence of pooled behavioral estimates, general characterizations of the individual in terms of intensity of reaction, persistence, rhythmicity, etc. are identified. Since no assumption is made about the specificity of drives or motives, attributes of functioning may be compared without doing violence to logic or fact at every developmental level.

Once children can be identified in terms of their functional styles, it is possible to study the interrelation of the child's characteristics to the environment in his development. Such study need no longer be based upon vague and general concepts of constitutional type, but instead may take its start from concrete knowledge of the child's actual initial characteristics of reactivity. One can move from a one-sided concern with extrinsic influences on development to a consideration of development as a continuously interactive process.

Thus far it is clear that in our studies we have avoided any active concern with the problem of the sources for or etiology of primary patterning of reactivity. Consideration of etiology was deliberately deferred until we could clarify what it was that required etiologic explanation. It appeared pointless to seek sources for initial individuality before developing a body of methods, knowledge, and techniques which could permit the valid and reliable identification of primary reactive characteristics as such. However, since we are now able to characterize children with respect to their primary reactive patternings, a next and necessary step is the consideration of the sources from which such individuality in initial behavioral patterning may derive.

Several hypotheses may be advanced as to etiologies for initial difference in behavioral style. Most prominent are those represented in the following listing:

1]   Genetic familial.
2]   Prenatal influences.
3]   Paranatal influences.
4]   Early life experiences, encompassed by the first two months of life.
5]   Any combination of the above four possibilities.

On the basis of the data currently available, no firm ground exists for preferring any of the factors listed to any other. It is hoped that future investigations utilizing cross-cultural approaches, methods of co-twin control,* the identification of reactivity patterns in the neonate, the comparative study of the relation of prenatal and paranatal factors to reactivity type, and the study of initially characterized infants in standardized, stable foster home situations will provide the kinds of evidence that will make possible the identification of relevant etiologic variables. Once having obtained information on sources which contribute to initial individuality in reactivity, it will become necessary to explore the many possible mechanisms through which these influences may operate to affect behavior. As yet it is much too early to choose among endocrine, enzymatic, and neurophysiologic possibilities.

---

* A twin study [22] has recently been completed which supports the view that, in part, individuality may have a genetic basis.

REFERENCES

1. C. Singer, *Greek Biology and Greek Medicine* (Oxford: Oxford University Press, 1922).
2. W. H. Sheldon, S. S. Stevens, and W. B. Tucker, *The Varieties of Human Physique* (New York: Harper and Bros., 1940).
3. W. H. Sheldon and S. S. Stevens, *The Varieties of Temperament* (New York: Harper and Bros., 1942).
4. J. Locke, *An Essay Concerning Human Understanding* (New York: Dover Publications, 1959), I, Ch. 1.
5. S. Freud, *A General Introduction to Psychoanalysis* (New York: Garden City Publishing Co., 1938).
6. L. B. Murphy, "Psychoanalysis and Child Behavior," Bulletin of the Menninger Clinic, 21:177 (1957).
7. A. Anastasi and J. P. Foley, Jr., *Differential Psychology* (New York: Macmillan Co., 1949).
8. L. Tyler, *The Psychology of Human Differences* (New York: Appleton-Century-Crofts, 1956).
9. J. Bowlby, "Maternal Care and Mental Health," World Health Organization, Monograph No. 3 (Geneva, 1951).
10. N. D. C. Lewis and B. Pacella, eds., *Modern Trends in Child Psychiatry* (New York: International Universities Press, 1945).
11. K. Soddy, ed., *International Symposium: Mental Health and Infant Development* (New York: Basic Books, 1956), I.
12. H. Bruch, "Parent Education or the Illusion of Omnipotence," *American Journal of Orthopsychiatry,* 24:723 (1954).
13. R. Spitz, "Relevancy of Direct Infant Observation," *Psychoanalytic Study of the Child,* 12:175 (1957).
14. J. Bowlby, "The Nature of the Child's Tie to His Mother," *International Journal of Psychoanalysis,* 39:350 (1958).
15. J. Bowlby, "Etiology and the Development of Object Relations," *International Journal of Psychoanalysis,* 41:313 (1960).
16. S. Escalona, "The Impact of Psychoanalysis Upon Child Psychology," *Journal of Nervous and Mental Diseases,* 126:429 (1958).
17. S. Escalona and G. M. Heider, *Prediction and Outcome; A Study in Child Development* (New York: Basic Books, 1959).
18. J. B. Richmond and E. L. Lipton, "Some Aspects of the Neurophysiology of the Newborn and Their Implications for Child Development," *Dynamic Psychopathology in Childhood,* eds. L. Jessner and E. Pavenstedt (New York: Grune and Stratton, 1959), p. 78.

19. M. Kris, "The Use of Prediction in a Longitudinal Study," *Psychoanalytic Study of the Child,* 12:175 (1957).

20. J. D. Benjamin, "Prediction and Psychopathologic Theory," *Dynamic Psychopathology in Childhood,* eds. L. Jessner and E. Pavenstedt, *op. cit.*

21. D. M. Levy, "Experiments on the Sucking Reflex and Social Behavior of Dogs," *American Journal of Orthopsychiatry,* 4:203 (1934).

22. M. Rutter, S. Korn, and H. G. Birch, "Genetic and Environmental Factors in the Development of Primary Reaction Patterns," *British Journal of Clinical and Social Psychology.* [In preparation.]

VIII

Practical Implications

ANY STUDY of the sources of psychological individuality has practical implications. The finding that each child has an individual pattern of primary reactivity, identifiable in early infancy and persistent through later periods of life, must be considered seriously by everyone with responsibility for effective socialization of the child.

In general, this finding of initial and persisting reactivity patterns implies that all the infants will not respond in the same fashion to a given environmental influence. Rather, given constancy of environmental factors, the reaction will vary with the characteristics of the child upon whom the relatively constant stimulus is brought to bear. Specifically, the tactics utilized by parents or others in child rearing will have different behavioral results depending on the nature of the child to whom they are applied. This holds true for all aspects of the child's functioning: his response to feeding, sleep routines, and bath in the first year of life; his interaction with parents, siblings, and playmates as he grows older; and his reaction to situations of special stress, such as illness, radical changes in living conditions, or abrupt shifts in geographic environment. Whether weaning is early or late, toilet training is rigid or permissive, his mother hostile or overprotective, the characteristics of the child's behavior will be influenced by his primary reaction pattern as well as by his environment. In each new situation he faces his behavior will depend, in part at least, on whether his reactive style is primarily positive or negative, mild or of high intensity, rhythmic or arhythmic. This view of the child stands in contrast to the assumption that environmental influences as such have determinative effects.

It is certainly true that such factors as maternal overprotection or rejection, a punitive approach by the father, and sibling rivalry have been found to be associated with disturbances in the psychological development of the child. In addition, it has been demonstrated that environmental influences outside the immediate family, such as the school situation and the general social and cultural environment, play a significant part in influencing child development. Such findings have resulted in a tendency to approach child care practices almost exclusively with a focus on environmental factors. For the young child this has meant an emphasis on the role of the mother, and secondarily, of the father and siblings. For the older child there has been an additional focus on the school and various play situations. In analyses of normal child development or of psychological disturbances ranging from temper tantrums to delinquency or severe personality disorders, the central variable considered has been that of the behavior and attitude of the parent. Differences between children, whether they be well-adjusted kindergartners or angry adolescents, have been assumed to be almost exclusively the result of their parents, or a combination of this central parental force with especially stressful environmental factors.

Underlying the environmental approach is the assumption that all children will tend to react similarly to the same developmental influences. This has resulted in a search for the right set of rules, or no-rules, for bringing up baby. Our findings suggest that exclusive emphasis on the role of the environment in child development tells only part of the story and that responses to any regimen will vary in accordance with primary patterns of reactivity. It follows, therefore, that there can be no universally valid set of rules that will work equally well for all children everywhere.

Two case histories serve to illustrate the manner in which primary reactive characteristics may affect the infant's organization of behavior in feeding under self-demand conditions. One neonate fell asleep after two and a half ounces and was awake and crying in three and a half hours. His crying stopped only for a moment when he was picked up; it continued until the bottle was introduced into his mouth. At other times he might cry in between feedings; he would be found to be wet or soiled, and if changed, he would go back to sleep. Whether the last evening bottle was given as usual or was held off in the hopes of a larger meal and a longer sleep, the baby woke after the same three-and-a-half- to four-hour interval and cried until fed. The implications for child care practices are clear. This infant has a rhythmical pattern; he is intense, persistent, and nondistractible. The sooner the mother trains herself to follow his pattern of rhythmicity and to identify his needs, the sooner will her nurturing become more effective and satisfying to the infant.

A second infant fed inconsistently. Sleep was irregular. When he cried he could be quieted by stimuli such as rocking or holding. Frequently it was difficult to identify his need when he cried, since he was not wet, soiled, or apparently hungry, overclothed, or cold. For this infant optimum care practices could not be identical with those optimal for the first. Since the child did not have good rhythmicity or specific responses to defined conditions of need, it would be exceedingly difficult, if not impossible, for the mother to train herself to follow his rhythms or identify his needs. When an attempt was made to pursue a self-demand feeding schedule, the result was chaos and a complete disruption of family life. Peace was restored upon instituting a strictly scheduled regimen. When a measured amount of food was given and strict timing of meals observed, he rapidly formed habit patterns which were consistent with normal parental and societal requirements.

Fortunately for the parents the majority of the children in our group showed patterns involving adaptability with reactions of moderate and graded intensity. Our evidence suggests that within broad limits such babies did well with differing child care practices, as long as a given parent was consistent in approach. Accordingly, the application of a self-demand regimen resulted in the ready acquisition of acceptable patterns of socialization. It would be anticipated, however, that the course of habit acquisition and the development of desired behaviors and skills in the modal group of children would have been acquired with comparable ease had a more structured regimen been applied. Very likely it is this group of children that represents the substantial basis for the support of claims made concerning the efficacy of different child-rearing strategies.

From decade to decade child care practices have varied widely, and all in their time have been advocated by authorities as being clearly applicable to children's needs. While there has always tended to be a small group of youngsters whose behavior was not in keeping with the predicted outcome, a striking variety of practices seems to have been assimilated equally well by children of different periods, cultures, and classes. An examination of one aspect of the data of the present study may have bearing on this phenomenon. As has been noted, certain of the categories when examined in the preponderance model of analysis appear to characterize the group of children as a whole. This means that in certain respects children tend to behave preponderantly alike, and one can say of such behaviors that most children as a group behave in a specific fashion. There still remains the minority who do not behave in the modal manner of the group as a whole. In addition, within the modal group there are individual differences of degree of preponderance of a given behavior.

This finding has certain implications for child care practices, and indeed goes far in explaining why so many divergent modes of child care have been assimilable by the majority of children. The categories in which a modal point on the scale characterized the study group as a whole are adaptability, rhythmicity, and mood. Most of the children were regular rather than irregular, highly adaptable rather than unadaptable, and preponderantly positive in mood. Whatever the child care practice, the children would, as a whole, be capable of adapting, as long as the particular mode of handling the child was compatible with life.

In certain respects a variety of child care practices may be equally helpful with an equal proportion of youngsters. However, the small proportion of children who fail to adapt and thrive with one type of child care practice may be totally different from those who fail to thrive with another type of practice. During the centuries when infants were fed whenever they were hungry, most children apparently adapted to this approach. When feeding by the clock according to a predetermined schedule became the advocated pattern, most children adapted to this. When once again it was decided to feed children when they were hungry—now called "self-demand feeding"—in response to the awareness that a small group of children did not adapt to clock feeding, again most, but not all, children adapted to this method. While it is likely that those who failed to adapt to clock feeding had idiosyncratic behavioral characteristics dissimilar to those who failed to adapt to demand feeding, the majority of infants can adapt to either type of timing.

The enormous variety of child care practices which have succeeded in maintaining the race does not, however, attest to the equality of excellence. With the understanding that no general rule of child care practice will be appropriate for every child, it nevertheless can be argued that some general rules will be optimal for a higher percentage of children than other modes of practice. Defining such optimal practices still remains a goal, even though it will always be necessary to deviate from such general rules with some children.

The youngsters for whom the prescribed child care practice proves to be incompatible require an analysis of their primary characteristics of reactivity and an individually planned modification of the favored practice. It should be borne in mind that, while the unadaptable, irregular child of negative mood is a departure from the average, such a child is not thereby pathologic.

Sleeping patterns, their disruption and reinstatement, provide an especially rich area for exploring individuality. During infancy a variety of factors, including teething, minor illnesses, and environmental changes, may serve to disrupt a regular sleeping pattern. Two broad groups of children could be distinguished in our study population. One was characterized by ready adaptability, easy distractibility, and a high level of rhythmicity. Such infants responded to parental comforting during a period of upset by rapidly establishing a pattern of interrupted sleep in the period immediately following the disturbance. However, a brief retraining period in which no comforting response was made by the parent to the episodic crying resulted in the reestablishment of the initial pattern of regularity and uninterrupted sleep. The second group consisted of children whose primary reactive characteristics included high intensity, persistence, nondistractibility, and relatively poor adaptability. Such children did not so readily establish a new patterning of interrupted sleep as a consequence of disturbing circumstances. However, once a new sleep pattern was established, considerable and prolonged difficulty characterized the retraining course. In the main it appeared that the reactive characteristics of the child, and not the attitude of the mother, determined the course of events. The mother's attitudes, including insecurity or feelings of guilt, might determine how consistently she could initiate and sustain a retraining for the correction of departures from normal patterning. But it did not determine the rate of change in reaction by the child once the mother had instituted such a procedure.

The need to consider the child's individuality was equally apparent when studying responses to the teaching of prohibitions, or to attempts at toilet training. Babies with reaction patterns involving predominantly positive responses, easy adaptability, and easy distractibility were readily trained. However, they were simultaneously in danger of becoming inhibited and submissive if parental authority was exercised rigidly and involved excessive pressure. At the other extreme were the babies with predominantly negative responses to new stimuli and the tendency to be nonadaptive and nondistractible. Training was difficult to achieve in such children. Further, marked rigidity of parental approach also tended to produce negativistic reactions in these children. A combination of firmness, patient repetition, and flexibility in knowing when to retreat before provoking and fixating negativistic reactions was the most successful training procedure with this type of child.

The problem of readiness for new experiences and new demands bears a relation of special importance to individuality in characteristics of reactivity. The identification of the times of life that are most appropriate for the introduction of solid foods, for starting toilet training, and for beginning weaning with the expectation of smooth progress and successful accomplishment are all persistent problems arising in the consideration of child-rearing approaches. As a rule, serious treatments of the problem of readiness recognize individual differences among infants in a general way and express this in terms of the view that a range of ages (sometimes fairly wide) exists for each accomplishment and successful effort to control behavior. In our own samples of children individual differences in primary reactivity appeared to influence the ages at which different children could be successfully subjected to training procedures. Children with clear-cut rhythmicity in elimination, other things being equal, were far more readily toilet trained than were those children in whom evacuation occurred irregularly and with no clear-cut temporal patterning. In general, successful training in children who were arhythmic occurred when verbal functioning was sufficiently advanced so that the child could be informed as to the function for which he was being trained and was himself able to communicate his need to evacuate.

Awareness of characteristics of primary reactivity is particularly important when working with youngsters who present behavioral disturbances. Maladaptation of children, expressed in behavior disorders, is frequently discussed in terms of defensive reactions to inappropriate parental handling. But when one has succeeded in describing primary behavioral characteristics of given children, it becomes possible to examine the patterns that preceded the problem behavior. In the children of the present study it has been noteworthy that the maladaptive patterns have represented in many cases a caricature of the premorbid pattern; in others there has been a reversal of specific behaviors that had been characteristic prior to the appearance of disturbance in functioning. At times, in the same child, one characteristic has been extended to the point of caricature while another has been reversed. These findings carry their own implications for child care practices, and consequently have been examined for clues as to the sequences and causes of their occurrence.

It has been possible to see the development of the caricature of the initial pattern as the child interacted with his environment. The direction of possible inappropriate and unproductive behavior deviation cannot be definitely predicted, inasmuch as the fortuitous nature of environmental happenings plays a part along with family attitudes and parental handling. An example might be a child whose long attention span and persistent involvement with play activities made it possible for his mother to pursue her own interest for long periods undisturbed. With the introduction of the child to nursery school, minor tantrums began to occur along with his continued ability to involve himself in learning and play activities for long periods. In general, the tantrums occurred when change of activity was demanded by school routine. The next year, in first grade, with the teacher making decisions as to the timing and nature of activities, there was a daily period of disruptive behavior. It also became clear, in scrutinizing the maternal handling of this child, that he had been afforded little or no opportunity to learn to distinguish between legitimate selection of his own activity and situations when the demands of the environment should take precedence. Because of his quiet manner, his mother tended to ignore his demands upon her. This resulted in tantrum behavior which became his prime effective mode of demand. This pattern came to be transferred to the school situation.

In this child we see both caricature and reversal. The element of persistence was converted into a caricature. It was exploited indiscriminately by the mother without regard to the appropriateness of the situation. Response to the child occurred, not when he was persistent in his attention to an ongoing play activity, but when the same degree of persistence was expressed in prolonged tantrum behavior.

The reversal was apparent in the intensity of responses. During his first year of life, mild intensity was preponderant; by the second year, before the overt appearance of the behavior problem, he became preponderantly intense in his responses. It still remained characteristic of the child that he engaged quietly in a pursuit which claimed his positive attention. However, as mildly expressed desires found no response, and as instances multiplied when he was required to end an activity prematurely (for him), there was an increase in the number and proportion of situations to which he reacted negatively and intensely.

The caricature maladaptation was most clearly seen in those children whose normal pattern included initial withdrawal to new situations followed by positive approach after acclimatization. As demands multiplied for involvement with new groups of children or new places, the length of time needed for acclimatization often proved too great for productive interaction—the visit was almost over, the time allotment for the class activity came to an end, the other children were tired of the activity and went on to a different one before a shift from withdrawal to approach had occurred. In place of experiencing positive involvement, with the period of initial withdrawal being a negligible aspect, the child experienced instance after instance in which he was the outsider and onlooker. In time his behavior came to be characterized more by withdrawal than by participation.

It is apparent, too, from our study that the child's primary reaction pattern may influence, not only his own behavior, but also his parents' immediate and persistent attitude toward him. Where the child's primary pattern has made his care easy, the mother has often shown a much quicker and more intense development of positive attitudes than is manifested where the child's primary reactions have made his care more difficult and time-consuming. This influence of the child on the parental attitude has been most dramatically evident in two families whose twin children showed differences in initial and subsequent patterning of reactivity. In each family the mother started with the same general maternal attitude toward the two infants but developed increasingly dissimilar affective bonds and responses to them as they grew older. In large part these differences in attitude could be accounted for by the mother's reaction to initial differences in reactivity.

In one of these two sets of twins one child was very persistent in her functioning and difficult to distract. Her twin sister was less persistent and more distractible. The mother had a strong positive involvement with both children in early infancy. As they grew older, the persistent, nondistractible child responded to the usual parental demands for the learning of various prohibitions and for the adaptation to the social routines of the family with resistance and even negativism. The mother reacted to the child's pattern with antagonism and called the issue "a personal duel" between them. The less persistent and more distractible twin responded to the same parental demands with quick adaptation. The mother's reaction to her involved a continuation of the positive benign feeling previously evident toward both children.

In the other set of twins one child showed initial approach responses, positive mood, and intense reactivity. The twin sister showed withdrawal, mild reactivity, and more negative mood responses than did her twin. The mother, a detached and easily confused individual, found it difficult to assess accurately her children's needs and demands as manifested by their reactions. It was relatively easy for her to understand and satisfy the twin whose reactions were primarily positive and of an approaching character and who expressed her desires intensely. On the other hand, she frequently felt confused in coping with the other twin's mildly expressed negative reactions and frequent withdrawal responses. She labeled the first child as healthy and the second as a problem child. Even though the objective evidence did not confirm this differential labeling, she continued to be fixed in this judgment as the children grew older.

These findings raise several interesting questions about the interrelation of general parental attitude and child characteristics in the evolution of the parent-child relationship. Given any degree of ambivalence toward the parental role, the characteristics of the child may foster and reinforce a specific direction of parental attitude and practice. It is easy to mother a mildly active, positively responsive, highly adaptive, rhythmic child whose mood is predominantly cheerful. It is quite another matter to sustain the same positive maternal responses toward a highly active, negatively responsive, nonadaptive, arhythmic child whose mood is expressed by a preponderance of crying. The reciprocal dynamics of the parent-child interrelation have been insufficiently explored in child development and represent a most fruitful area for investigation.

The knowledge that certain characteristics of their child's development are not primarily due to parental malfunctioning has proven helpful to many parents. Mothers of problem children often develop guilt feelings because they assume that they are solely responsible for their children's emotional difficulties. This feeling of guilt may be accompanied by anxiety, defensiveness, increased pressures on the children, and even hostility toward them for "exposing" the mother's inadequacy by their disturbed behavior. When parents learn that their role in the shaping of their child is not an omnipotent one, guilt feelings may lessen, hostility and pressures may tend to disappear, and positive restructuring of the parent-child interaction can become possible.

Illustrative Cases and Scoring

THIS APPENDIX provides illustrative behavioral items from various parental interview protocols which constitute scorable items for the three scale points for each of the nine categories. The illustrations are quoted verbatim from the records.

As may be seen below, six of the categories are divided into subcategories for the purposes of scoring. The scored items are recorded under the appropriate subcategories, and the total score for the category as a whole is obtained by the addition of all the subscores. Functional subcategories could not be developed for the quality of mood and distractibility. Attention span items and persistence items are scored separately, also without the use of subcategories, and the two scores are then summated to obtain the score for this category as a whole.

I. ACTIVITY LEVEL

Subcategories include motility, wake/sleep, eating, and exploring and quality of play.

A. MOTILITY

high

a. Stands in tub, very active, splashes, won't stay seated.
b. Walks actively, bounces up and down a lot.
c. Scoots all over crib since second week, also in sleep.

moderate

a. Enjoys bath. Smiles, gurgles, moves a moderate amount.

b. Began to smile as she approached the beach and played cautiously in the water.

c. Kicks and moves arms. Moves in sleep.

low

a. Does not move much in sleep.

b. Very passive in bath. Moves very little.

c. Very sluggish the first three weeks. Still not very active, though no longer sluggish. Moves very little in sleep.

B. WAKE/SLEEP The activity level here is scored according to the proportion of wakeful to sleep periods.

high

a. Not a big sleeper. Awakens early. Today he awakened at 5:00 A.M.

b. Since arriving at home, he would not go to sleep after nursing. Fussed up to two hours, even with patting or rocking while lying down.

c. Getting him to bed "a tour de force." He's in and out. We hit, cajole. May be put to bed either 7:30 or 8:30. Takes up to 9:30 before he's asleep. But no matter what time he is put to sleep, he always awakens at the same time, 6:30 A.M. He is picked up at 11:00 P.M. for changing. About twice a week or more he awakens when changed and can stay up for as long as three hours. He's wide awake. This staying awake again has no effect on early morning awakening, which is always 6:30.

moderate

a. For a two-week period ending one and a half weeks ago, he awakened a half to three quarters of an hour after going to sleep, either played for an hour and went back to sleep or cried until given bottle. He took two to three ounces and went back to sleep.

b. Two months ago he started crying at night one to two times a week. Parent goes in, pats him, he goes back to sleep. Occasionally he is standing up crying, short hug puts him back to sleep.

low

a. To bed between 6:30 and 7:00 P.M. Goes to sleep without any fuss or special routine. Sleeps through night. Gets up between 7:30 and 8:00 A.M.

b. At two and a half months he slept through 2:00 A.M. feeding. Two weeks later, at the doctor's suggestion, he was not awakened for 10:00 P.M. feeding and slept from 6:00 P.M. to 6:00 A.M. Has done this since, doesn't awaken at night at all.

c. Now sleeps to 7:00–7:30 A.M. If she has four bottles by 7:00 P.M., she will sleep through the morning.

C. EATING   The activity level is scored here according to the vigor of eating, sucking, and quantity of intake.

high

a. Active sucker.

b. Eats like a horse, eats everything, including all kinds of new foods, no dislikes.

c. Eats everything with gusto.

d. My problem is getting it into him fast enough. If not fast enough, his head starts bobbing around looking for it or his fingers go into his mouth.

moderate

a. At present he takes full diet. He eats less meat than other foods and more vegetables.

b. Eats all solids, but refuses additional milk at end of meal.

c. In general, eats good amount. Eats best at supper. Breakfast and lunch are about the same in quantity from day to day. Supper intake is very variable.

low

a. Breast feeding was attempted the first three days in the hospital. The baby sucked poorly and fell asleep, and therefore it was discontinued.

b. Fell asleep after sucking one ounce. Food no more than two ounces at a time, then didn't suck, just kept nipple in mouth.

c. He doesn't relate to food. Mother has to sit and push food in his mouth, most of which is accepted.

D. EXPLORING AND QUALITY OF PLAY

high

a. Chins on window, crib, or carriage. Pulls self off feet.

b. In Taylor-Tot, she moves quickly, backs, turns in tight places. If refrigerator door opens, she may come in Taylor-Tot at lightning speed from another room.

c. Very positive reaction to dog. Reaches out to him, crawls after him, tries to play with him.

d. In the playpen, on the floor, and in the Taylor-Tot, pulls out books, turns on television, finds pieces of thread and chews them.

moderate

a. In playpen can entertain self for a half to one hour. Takes things apart and puts them together, talks to them, pulls herself up and lowers herself down, taking more and more toys in her hands and mouth.

b. Extremely cautious. Won't climb up the stairs of slide. Wants to go on from bottom of the slide. Doesn't attempt to ride tricycle, gets on but wants to be pushed. Climbs up on couch and table.

low

a. Can play by himself for even an hour in crib, then usually goes to sleep right away.

b. Mother puts him in playpen when she thinks he needs change. If put in without toys, just watches people moving or looks at objects.

c. In the park he does whatever the other children are doing. He never grabs, usually the other way around. He looks hurt. Mother feels he is too passive.

II. RHYTHMICITY

Subcategories include wake/sleep, hunger, activity periods, bowel function, and food ingestion.

A. WAKE/SLEEP

regular

a. At 8:00 P.M. is placed in bed with soft wool blanket, mother sits and gives bottle, sings and talks, may finish or refuse some, turns her back and curls up. Awakens at 8:00 A.M., occasionally fifteen minutes earlier or later.

b. To bed between 6:30 and 7:00 P.M. Goes to sleep without fuss or special routine. Gets up between 7:30 and 8:00 A.M.

c. Not awakened for 10:00 P.M. feeding, and slept right through 6:00 P.M. to 6:00 A.M. Has done this since, doesn't awaken at night.

irregular

a. No schedule. Has been varying time quite a bit. Awakens earlier, today he awoke at 5:00 A.M.

b. To sleep between 6:30 and 7:00 P.M. Slept till 2:00–4:00 A.M. After that feeding didn't go to sleep for thirty minutes. Sometimes stayed up until next feeding at 10:00 A.M.

c. Bedtime irregular since past two months. Time from 8:00 P.M. to 10:00 P.M.

B. HUNGER

regular

a. Feeding during day on demand, regular.
b. Every three-and-a-half- to 4-hour schedule from beginning.
c. At first on three hours. When amount of concentration of formula increased, he went to every four hours within a few days.

irregular

a. After coming home he was put on self-demand. Woke up at two- to four-hour intervals, not very regular.
b. Three meals, no regular hours. Depends on awakening and on sleep during day.
c. Will wait for meals at convenience of mother, any amount of time; Sunday until 10:00 A.M.

C. ACTIVITY PERIODS Regularity here is scored according to the pattern of the napping schedule, which indicates regularity of activity and rest periods.

regular

a. Long morning nap and shorter afternoon nap, fairly regular.
b. Sleeps an hour after 10:00 A.M. feeding. In afternoon, sleeps from about 4:00 to 6:00 P.M.
c. Two- to two-and-a-half-hour nap, right after lunch.

irregular

a. Day naps irregular. She can't judge his nap time. He wouldn't go to sleep much in the morning, and too difficult to get to sleep in afternoon. Would cry and want to get out, so she tried one nap sometime during day.
b. Time of naps in the morning varies. Put in and may play or fall asleep. Not too definite as to time. Duration: one to two hours. This is the only nap unless it's a rainy day, and he may sleep again or fall asleep outdoors.

D. BOWEL FUNCTION

regular

a. One to two bowel movements a day, regular, usually in morning.
b. One bowel movement per day, during night.
c. Usually one bowel movement a day, mostly an hour after 6:00 A.M. feeding.

irregular

a. One to three bowel movements a day, quite irregular.

b. Has one bowel movement a day, timing irregular.

c. Mother doesn't put him on potty consistently because she never knows when he has a bowel movement.

E. FOOD INGESTION (REGULARITY OF AMOUNT)

regular

a. Three regular meals a day, no extra bottle.

b. Food intake regular from day to day. Preferences are consistent.

c. Eats three regular meals, not much in between; mother limits because of weight.

irregular

a. He doesn't relate to food unless he really wants it. At times he eats no breakfast. Lunch seems like best meal, but occasionally he doesn't eat lunch if he has had a midmorning snack. Sometimes eats a sandwich, and sometimes only takes a bite of it.

b. Breakfast and lunch best meal. Dinner irregular as to quantity. Quantity eaten at breakfast and lunch varies, more or less.

c. Quantity varies from day to day and meal to meal and even with same food.

variability in regularity For any of the above subcategories, an item of behavior was scored as variable if there was evidence that the child had established a pattern of functioning but that there was some deviation from this pattern on occasion. This designation stands in contrast to a score of irregular, which denoted the failure to establish even a partial pattern.

a. One to two bowel movements a day, varies in the morning. This was scored as regular and varied.

b. Baby brought to mother every three hours. Sometimes he nursed well; at other times he was sleepy and didn't take much. This was scored as regular and varied.

c. To bed at 7:30. Two thirds of the time she goes right to sleep. Other nights she fights going to bed. This was scored as regular and varied.

d. Afternoon nap if he is at home. If he goes outdoors, he may or may not take a nap. This was scored as regular and varied.

e. Most meals are regular about 90 percent of time. Week-end timing is different. This was scored as regular and varied.

III. APPROACH-WITHDRAWAL

Scorable items are obtained from the nature of the child's response to the initial contact with a new stimulus. Subcategories include people, toys, situations, foods, and places.

A. PEOPLE

approach

a. His response to strangers is positive; he smiles, talks, bounces, stands up and dances in carriage, looks at everyone, especially children.
b. Friendly, greets everyone at door. Greets people at stoplight. Says "hi" to children and adults. Greets most strangers, walking up to them and saying hello.
c. Very friendly. Makes overtures, persists with these until he gets a response.

withdrawal

a. When he is with strangers and mother is holding him, he clings and averts his head.
b. Sudden appearance of stranger will cause crying and running away (crawling). With any stranger he will cry and move in direction of mother.

B. TOYS

approach

a. If he is given a toy, especially if it is a new toy, he will stop crying and play with it.
b. Goes to new toys immediately, usually to neglect of old toys.

withdrawal

a. Was afraid at first of new toy horse. Started to cry.
b. When placed on sled, he stiffened and wouldn't sit on it.

C. SITUATIONS

approach

a. Smiles, sticks tongue out, and licks washcloth while having face washed.
b. Enjoys hair brushing, laughs.
c. Very positive reaction to dog. Reaches out to him, crawls after him, tries to play with him.

d. Enjoyed first bath, smiled, gurgled. Moved a moderate amount.

withdrawal

a. At eight months, whimpered and fussed a great deal when first brought to beach, even before put in water. Had to be taken away.
b. At nine weeks, taken to Chicago by plane due to death of a grandparent. Routine disturbed. His sleeping became irregular, cried a great deal. Disturbances became greater as they stayed over the four days.
c. First bath at two weeks, hated it, screamed.
d. During facewashing, turns head, cries, pushes mother's hand away.

D. FOODS

approach

a. Solids—first cereal at about five to six weeks. Took it without any fussing. Has taken it well since.
b. Tried orange juice a month ago. Took it well from beginning.
c. Vitamin drops started at three weeks. Made sucking movements, took it well from beginning.
d. Likes new food first time. Continues to accept when offered.

withdrawal

a. Vitamin drops started at one week. Made faces, tried to spit it out, sometimes cried.
b. Orange juice started yesterday. Diluted in water in bottle. Had been taking water from bottle. Spit out nipple, made face, and cried.
c. When given beets, he gagged a bit and spit some out. He didn't cry. He spit green vegetables out.
d. Rarely tastes new food. Won't let it get into mouth by saying "no" or brushing it away, or may spit it out.

E. PLACES

approach

a. In country for two and a half months. No problem of adjustment. Had been taken there several weekends before, also with immediate adjustment.
b. Has been back and forth to Pennsylvania three times. Slept on train each time. No apparent reaction to change in room or crib. Will go to sleep on bed other than his own.
c. Slept at grandparents. Slept very well. No difference in pattern. No effect on sleep.

d. Moving to a different apartment in the same building. No difference in eating or sleeping.

withdrawal

a. At nine months, spent five days at Montauk Point. Had to sleep in carriage. He cried all day; at night parents walked the carriage to put him to sleep.
b. In park and in store is silent and clings to mother in past weeks. Mother thinks this last change has occurred because they have moved to new apartment. Also awake first few nights crying after this move.
c. Taken on trip in car. Did not fall asleep in car during ride. Upset, whining, complaining.

variability in approach-withdrawal For any of the above sub-categories, an item of behavior was scored as variable if there was evidence that the child had an initial approach or withdrawal response but with some deviation from this response.

a. Situations: No objection unless sleepy, when he will cry. This was scored as approach and varied.
b. People: Strangers are watched seriously, then she warms up and eventually goes to them if they keep their distance. If they come too fast, she pulls back and may even cry. This was scored as withdrawal and varied.
c. Toys: Sometimes takes new toy, sometimes not. This was scored as approach and varied.

IV. ADAPTABILITY

Subcategories include food, noises, mother substitutes, places, toys, procedures, and sleep habits.

A. FOOD

adaptive

a. Previous negative reactions to some foods, such as applesauce and peas, have disappeared. Now takes them all well.
b. Mother gave her primarily the sweet fruits. Occasionally she slipped in the others. Now takes them all well.

nonadaptive

a. With table foods, such as fish and lamb chops, spits out the pieces and if given again spits out.
b. Only food rejected was tuna fish. Given three times, each time let it drool out, didn't spit, didn't fuss.
c. There are some foods he has consistently disliked, such as liver, tomato juice, and stews.

B. NOISES

adaptive

a. No reaction now to loud noises, used to cry.

b. Used to startle at noises, now less sensitive.

nonadaptive

a. Still startles sharply with any sudden loud noise. Will stop eating if faucet is dripping. Mother turns it off.

b. Picks head up, stops eating with bell, buzzer, radio. Cries for minute with sudden noises. Reaction has not changed.

C. MOTHER SUBSTITUTES

adaptive

a. Goes to bed for housekeeper equally well.

b. Stayed with grandmother for weekend and whole week during August. No change.

c. Recognizes nurse by voice. Turns toward voice, smiles, laughs when played with.

nonadaptive

a. At age twenty months, parents were away for one week, leaving child in the care of the housekeeper. Was listless and refused food, including bottle. He walked around sucking thumb and pajamas a good deal.

b. When left with grandparents, always fusses and cries until mother returns.

D. PLACES

adaptive

a. After three weeks at beach, tried again, starting with few minutes at back of beach and increasing time at two- to three-day intervals. Did fuss but could be distracted. Fussing decreased, and disappeared by fifth time. Then held on mother's lap in water a moment and was O.K. Immersion increased each time, no fussing. After five to six such trips into the water, she began to enjoy it. Began to smile as she approached beach, and played in water. Positive reaction continued in this way.

b. After moving to new house, she cried a few minutes first few nights when put to bed in new room. No crying since then.

nonadaptive

a. Moved to new apartment two weeks ago. Still cries for fifteen minutes each night when put to bed.

b. At beach this summer, cried and pulled back each time we tried to put her in the water. We gave up trying after a week.

E. TOYS

adaptive

a. Afraid at first with new toy horse. Mother lets him approach by himself. Now he asks to be put on.

b. Has about twenty stuffed animals. Mother took some away with his agreement. Some time later (mother hadn't given them away), he made a big to-do when he saw animals and told her he didn't want to give any away.

nonadaptive

a. Never plays with toy trucks or cars, even though he has many of them.

b. Cried when given stuffed dog. Still cries when he sees it.

F. PROCEDURES

adaptive

a. First bath, very passive. Didn't yell or anything, but also didn't seem particularly happy. Now likes it, kicks and gurgles.

b. Medication O.K. now. Doesn't fuss with nose drops as before.

c. Now cooperates in dressing, moves arms helpfully. Doesn't twist and turn away as he used to.

nonadaptive

a. First haircut O.K. After that, squirmed, cried.

b. When dressing, not interested, not cooperative. Yells to show he doesn't want to get dressed.

c. Diapering is a battle.

G. TRAINABILITY

adaptive

a. If told "no," obeys. Will go up to prohibited object, and, before mother says anything, will shake her head "no" and avoid it.

b. She is easily trained to do specific tasks. New things are taught without a bit of effort.

c. Trained with bowel movement and daytime urination. Wipes self; goes to bathroom on her own. This occurred in late spring, although mother not sure exactly when.

nonadaptive

a. Not toilet trained. When has bowel movement, goes into his room, takes pajamas out of his drawer (just takes them out, does not put them on), gets a book, stands, and has a bowel movement. Is still in diapers. Will not have bowel movement sitting down. If picked up while he is defecating, screams. Stops when put down.

b. Not supposed to roll on bedspread or jump up and down. He's smacked. Stops at the time, but does it again.

c. Even on items such as putting plug in electric socket, does it over and over despite repeated "no's." Does not seem affected by limits and rules on things he really wants to do. If stopped, may get angry and throw or slam.

H. SLEEP HABITS

adaptive

a. Has slept at grandparents, but not frequently. Slept very well. No difference in pattern. No effect on sleep.

b. As soon as he got home, returned to regular sleeping pattern.

c. Has been back and forth to Pennsylvania three times. Slept on train each time, no apparent change in room or crib. Will go to sleep on bed other than his own.

nonadaptive

a. Took a number of days after return home to get back to usual routine. Cried a lot, and sleeping was irregular.

b. At nine weeks, taken to Chicago by plane. Routine disturbed. His sleeping became irregular. Cried a good deal and insistently. Disturbances became greater as they stayed over the four days.

variability in adaptability   For any of the above subcategories, an item of behavior was scored as variable if an adaptive or nonadaptive response had occurred but with some variation in the other direction.

a. If told "no," usually obeys, except that once in a while he will not listen. This was scored as adaptive and variable.

b. Once in a while he will take medicine, but mostly he still screams and kicks. This was scored as nonadaptive and variable.

c. Now toilet trained in the daytime, except that every two to three days has an accident. This was scored as adaptive and variable.

V. INTENSITY OF REACTION

Subcategories include sensory stimuli, internal states, new foods, diapering and dressing, attempts to control, bath, play, and social.

A. SENSORY STIMULI This includes reactions to auditory and visual stimuli, being wet, and having temperature taken.

intense

a. If he is wet, he cries. Stops when changed.
b. Cries loudly at the noise of hammering. Cries loudly at the sound of thunder.
c. Fears loud unfamiliar and familiar sounds. For example, on return from vacation to New York City, during fire siren and elevator noise, ran to mother and placed head on her lap. Was terrified. One couldn't pry her head off the lap, it was buried so intensely.
d. Screamed and kicked when temperature was taken, even though it was done with explanation and game. Cried all along.

mild

a. Very light sleeper. Easily awakened by sound or light. No startle to loud noises.
b. In bright sunlight, closes eyes and turns head.
c. The baby stops her play to listen to such sounds as fire engines and barking of dog.
d. When diaper is wet, only fusses a little bit.

B. INTERNAL STATES This includes reactions to hunger, satiation, and bowel movement.

intense

a. When moving bowels, stiffens and screams.
b. If she is hungry and not fed immediately, she screams when placed in chair.
c. Rejects food by pushing food and mother's hand away. Very definite and violent.
d. Indicates satiation by shutting mouth tight, turning head, sweeping hand away.

mild

a. Satiation indicated by pushing mother's hand away.
b. Up to two months showed hunger by crying "soft cry," as if annoyed.
c. He enjoys himself before bowel movement. Not bothered. You can see his face get red.

d. When full, just leaves nipple in mouth, doesn't suck. Can't be induced to continue.

C. NEW FOODS

intense

a. Vitamin drops started at three weeks. Delighted. Made sucking movements. Took it well from the beginning.

b. Doesn't like the tart desserts, such as apricots and applesauce. Would push them out, spit, or cry.

mild

a. Liver started six to eight weeks ago. Took small spoonfuls, swallowed them, then shuddered. Made very wry face, but continued to take it.

b. When given beets, gagged a bit and spit some out. Didn't cry.

c. Took bananas and applesauce well from beginning. Screwed face up first time.

D. DIAPERING AND DRESSING

intense

a. During diaper changing, he is full of smiles. Helps by raising body, straightening legs. He is very excited.

b. Not cooperative. Yells to show he doesn't want to get dressed.

c. When being undressed, she wriggles and cries. She insists upon trying to undress herself. Resists being held still.

mild

a. Fusses momentarily when clothing pulled on over head.

b. If diaper is being changed and he has to be restrained, he does fuss a little.

c. Quite cooperative. Takes her socks off. Has tried to take shoes off.

E. ATTEMPTS TO CONTROL   Intensity of reaction is scored here on the basis of the intensity of the child's reaction to the parent's efforts to change or control behavior. These most usually occur in the areas of scheduling, training, and discipline.

intense

a. Gets angry if attempt is made to feed him. Moves head, throws own fork on floor, says "down" and tries to get out of chair, hands whole plate over.

b. Will not have bowel movement sitting down. If picked up while he is defecating, he screams. Stops when put down.

   c. When told "no" to something he wants or is intent on doing, will hit mother.

mild

   a. When parents are firm and really mean it, she obeys. Teases mother about this.

   b. If told "no," obeys. Will go to prohibited object, and, before mother says anything, will shake her head "no" and avoid it, or at most touch it briefly.

   c. To a firm parental "no," she stops, lowers head, and is absolutely silent.

F. BATH

intense

   a. She adored her bath. Greatest game in the world. Plays with toys very actively.

   b. First time at two weeks. Hated it, screamed. Continued till ten weeks—screamed through entire bath, drying, dressing, and powdering.

   c. Dislikes shampoo, screams, cries.

mild

   a. Seems to enjoy it, plays with toys. Does not mind if bath is skipped. Does not ask for it.

   b. Still in yellow plastic tub. Likes it, stands up, splashes, watches water running. Plays with washcloth. No objection to removal.

   c. Kicks a little in bath. Doesn't smile.

G. PLAY

intense

   a. Chooses his own books. Loves records, listens constantly. Asks mother to put it on. If it is one he doesn't like, he says, "no, no, new records." Stands and listens entranced.

   b. If toy is grabbed from him, cries loudly and fights back. He puts on quite a show. Grabs toys frequently from other children. Cries and fights hard if resisted.

   c. At times goes into spasm of laughter when nurse is playing with him roughly.

mild

   a. A child hit her and she looked surprised. Didn't hit back.

   b. With children his own age, there is watching. May imitate briefly, parallel play. Briefly waits his turn, and defers according to rule.

c. Plays alone. Enjoys having mother for reading and singing to him.

H. SOCIAL

intense

a. When a stranger or neighbor picks him up, he cries loudly.

b. It's wonderful. He runs up to every person on park bench, wakes up men that are sleeping. Talks and laughs with them.

c. As soon as he hears door slam and father arrives, crawls toward him, makes wild happy sounds, and starts to climb up on father. May cry if he sees anyone with coat on leaving.

c. Has a great interest in other children and dogs. Active interchange. Curious as to what they are doing. Yells a war whoop out of excitement and delight.

mild

a. She is definitely interested in strangers. She does not take initiative quickly, but will respond gradually to overtures made toward her.

b. When one or both parents leave, he simply says goodbye or opens the door for them. Occasionally he complains, especially if they leave abruptly after a playing session. He stops as soon as they have gone.

c. He makes overtures to strangers, but responds to the kind of response he gets—indifference with indifference, interest when showing things, or when initiating or participating in a game.

d. Approaches strangers, looks up at them, smiles. May not talk right away. Does not necessarily move toward children, but may follow what they do. Will stay with neighbors or friends when mother has to leave him. Lets mother go. When mother returns, greets her, but leaves her to resume play.

variability in intensity of reaction For any of the above subcategories, an item of behavior was scored as variable if there was evidence of variable intensity of response to the same type of stimulus.

a. Cries loudly when being dressed at bedtime, less at other times.

b. Sometimes laughs and jumps when approached by another child. At other times just smiles a little.

c. Dislikes hairwash, sometimes screams. But at other times just fusses a little.

VI. THRESHOLD OF RESPONSIVENESS

Subcategories include auditory, visual, and tactile as one subcategory, food, wet and soiled, social threshold, and discrimination.

A. AUDITORY, VISUAL, AND TACTILE

low

    a. Startles sharply at any sudden loud noise. Will stop eating if faucet is dripping, mother turns it off. Bounces up and down in rhythm to any tune she hears. Smiles as soon as music box is wound.

    b. In bright light, buries head; if can't, will close eyes and cry.

    c. Likes back rubbing and tickling. Laughs loudly.

moderate

    a. Jumps at loud noises. Doesn't cry.

    b. At night, no response to outside noises. During day "picks up ears" when fire siren goes by. She looks up, doesn't cry.

low

    a. No startle reaction to noises. No reaction to lights.

    b. Not bothered by loud noises. Not awakened by noise or light.

B. FOOD This includes degrees of preferences and dislikes, and reactions to different tastes and consistencies.

low

    a. He has strong likes and dislikes. Doesn't like noodles or spaghetti. He spits it out.

    b. Junior foods are rejected. He drools it out. If mashed and reoffered, he eats. He likes pureed meat, opens mouth for spoonfuls. Consistency is very important for cereal.

    c. Loves rich, heavy soup. Eats few starches except bread, but will eat potatoes and noodles in his soup. Loves all spicy foods. Mother tries varying his "love" for spicy food with other types. He barely eats others.

moderate

    a. Less enthusiastic about pureed vegetables. Likes pieces of bread. No longer likes zwieback.

    b. No negative reactions to food. Banana is still her favorite.

high

    a. Eats everything, including all kinds of new foods. No dislikes.

    b. No difference between breast and bottle.

    c. Cereal was started at three months, vegetables at four

months, meat and cheese at five months, and all were taken willingly. At six months, junior foods were taken willingly. Table foods were started at nine months and taken willingly.

C. WET AND SOILED

low

a. Cries or fusses when diaper is wet.
b. Violent objection to bowel movement. Cries to be changed right away. With bowel movement sometimes cries till actually cleaned, sometimes as soon as changing is started.

moderate

a. May or may not cry if he has a bowel movement.
b. Usually not bothered by wet diaper. At times, if he has been crying, a change of diaper will stop him.

high

a. No complaints with wetting.
b. Does not seem aware or mind being wet.
c. No objection to being wet or soiled.

D. SOCIAL THRESHOLD

low

a. When sees father, he looks. If hears key or footsteps, gives him a look, laughs, vocalizes, bounces, reaches.
b. Loves company. Greeting is verbal. Reserves hugs and kisses for later. He goes to children he knows. Plays immediately or he and children greet with big shriek of happiness.
c. Screamed when father first came out to country six weeks ago after few weeks absence.

moderate

a. Less responsive with older people, uneasy with them.
b. Smiles actively at mother, father, grandmother, and sister.
c. Takes a few minutes to warm up to strangers.

high

a. Can be left with anyone, anywhere; doesn't bother him.
b. Went to a different doctor in the summer. No reaction. Given injection, didn't cry at all.

E. DISCRIMINATION

low

a. Won't take cereal, spits it out. Even if mixed with applesauce, which he likes, still won't take it.

b. When mother or father make a change in dress or hairdo, she examines carefully and cautiously. She is especially cautious when they are wearing hats.

moderate

a. Won't take most vegetables unless mixed with a lot of sugar. A little sugar won't do.

b. Sleeps on stomach. Cries if put on back, unless very tired, when she will go to sleep on back or stomach.

high

a. Spits out meat, but if mixed with a little fruit, she takes it.

b. Sleeps on either stomach or back just as easily.

VII. *QUALITY OF MOOD*

No special subcategories are utilized for the scoring of this category.

positive mood

a. Enjoys bath. Splashes, plays, stands up.

b. At times goes into spasms of laughter when nurse is playing with him.

c. One week ago, rolled over from abdomen to back. Has been doing this more often, laughs.

d. When having face washed, smiles, sticks tongue out, and licks washcloth.

e. Has a big smile. Usually gives everyone a big smile, even before they smile at him.

f. Smiles actively at mother, father, grandfather, and sister.

negative mood

a. With foods she didn't like, would react often with crying. Takes some egg yolk, then starts whining.

b. Violent objection to bowel movement. Cries to be changed right away.

c. Fusses and cries with snowsuit and hat.

d. With a recent bout of diarrhea, she awoke several times during the night. Subsequently, for a week, she continued to awaken several times a night, crying and fussing.

e. Negative reaction to grandfather, who was noisy and rushed her.

f. When he is removed from tub, he cries. Cries when mother lays him down.

g. Sudden appearance of stranger causes crying and running away.

h. To a "no," he cries, but not intensely.

variable mood   This indicates a reaction varying between positive and negative for the same stimulus.

a. With a few familiar people, will smile spontaneously. This is the exception.
b. Easily responsive and friendly to strangers, especially in house. In park and store, is silent and clings to mother.
c. No objection to dressing and undressing, unless sleepy, then fusses.

VIII. DISTRACTIBILITY
No special subcategories are utilized for the scoring of this category.

distractible   On score cards and sheets distractible is listed as Yes (Y).

a. Occasionally, when night feeding was all set, and he had been in a feeding position, if bottle had to be cooled, he would cry, but could be quieted by talking.
b. When he stops eating, playing a game or singing will get him to open mouth and swallow a few more spoonfuls.
c. She can be distracted immediately from a tantrum by another activity.
d. If sung to, will stop crying.
e. Doesn't like being washed, unless an Indian noise game is made of it.
f. When held down for diapering, fusses, but is diverted with pacifier or toy.

nondistractible   On score cards and sheets nondistractible is listed as No (N).

a. Cries and struggles when dressing. Not easy to divert, becoming increasingly harder. Does not stop to singing or toy. Stops crying only when dressing is completed.
b. When force-fed medicine, cries for ten to fifteen minutes and can't be readily soothed. Will accept no food, no toy, no "nothing."
c. If something is taken from his reach, will cry. Not distractible with substitution.
d. If she is refused something she wants, screams and kicks for fifteen minutes. Nothing will distract her.

variability in distractibility   This indicates a reaction varying between distractible and nondistractible for the same stimulus.

a. Cries and twists away when dressed. Keeps on crying. Nothing distracts her, except once in a while her older sister can quiet her by talking to her and laughing.

b. When he has a tantrum, it just lasts a few moments and he is easily distracted with a toy or a game. But if he is sleepy, nothing distracts him.

c. When he's hungry and the bottle isn't ready, he cries loudly. He can be distracted by talking, but after a few minutes, he cries again. He can then be distracted a second time with a toy or by bouncing him.

IX. ATTENTION SPAN AND PERSISTENCE

Subcategories include attention span and persistence. On score cards and sheets long attention span and long persistence are listed as Yes (Y), and short attention span and short persistence are listed as No (N).

A. ATTENTION SPAN The categorization of attention span as long or short takes into consideration the age of the child and the type of activity.

long (yes)

a. Has learned to hit xylophone with drumstick. She kept to this with determination with father for fifteen minutes of learning.

b. In playpen can entertain self for a half to one hour. Takes things apart and puts them together, talks to them, pulls herself up and lowers herself down, taking more and more toys in her hands and mouth.

c. Enjoys singing, piano, listening to records, beanbag, drawing. He spends as much as thirty to sixty minutes on whatever he is doing.

d. In crib, will look at birds one and a half hours, frequently cooing.

short (no)

a. Very short attention span. Concentrates on a toy not at all or very little. If brother and father are reading, after five pages he tries to take book away if father continues with brother.

b. Has learned to do puzzles, but stays with this about five to ten minutes.

c. With difficult toy, gives up quite easily, fusses, and asks for help.

d. A book lasts five minutes.

variable

a. In playpen sometimes plays by herself with her toys for an hour. At other times she wants to be taken out after five minutes.

b. She can look at the same book, and turn pages for a half hour. At other times she is finished after five minutes.

B. PERSISTENCE

long (yes)

a. Now standing, crawling, edging around, holding on. Practiced a lot for three to four weeks before crawling and walking. Came gradually.

b. For breakfast refuses cereal and fruit, and yells and bangs until she is given her boiled egg.

c. Prefers milk. Has to have bottle first, never refused it. If solids offered first, takes and swallows first spoonful, then keeps mouth closed until bottle is offered.

d. He also asks how it is to be done and watches, does it a few times. Calls for help to be shown again and again if not successful. Persists until successful.

short (no)

a. Tries to take off shirt and pajama top. If can't do this, just stops.

b. Only tries turning himself over for a minute or two, then gives up. Able to do it suddenly, just came by itself.

c. Wants bottle first. If given cereal first, fusses a moment, then takes the cereal.

variable

a. With difficult puzzle sometimes tries for a long time. Sometimes gives up after a few minutes and asks for help.

b. Tries to take off socks, can't. Sometimes tries for fifteen minutes. Won't let anyone help him. At other times quits trying after a minute.

Three Complete Protocols and Scoring

THREE TYPICAL scored parental interview protocols are presented below. The protocols are for three different children: *1*] at three months; *2*] at one year; and *3*] at two years of age.

The behavioral data are detailed on the left side of the page. Phrases or sentences within quotation marks represent the mother's verbatim statements. The scorable items are italicized and numbered. The category scores for each item are directly to the right, with the numbers corresponding to the numbers of the item to the left. As may be seen, many items are scorable for two or more categories.

The category scores for the three protocols are tabulated at the end of this Appendix in Table 14. These scores are obtained by totaling the individual item scores.

A. *Child One, boy, age three months*

SLEEP: Came home at eight days. Mother started breast-feeding him twelve hours after birth. Baby brought to mother every three hours. Sometimes he nursed well; at other times sleepy and didn't take much. Nurses would say that he cried a lot between feedings after such a small feeding. After coming home, put on self-demand.

(1) *Woke up at two- to four-hour intervals, not very regular.* Slept through 10:00 P.M. time from first night at home. Up for 2:00 A.M. feeding, still true. At four weeks mother has tried waking him at 10:00 P.M. He nursed well, *(2, 3, 4) stayed up till 2:00 A.M. fussing.* Have not tried any changing of schedule since then.

(1) Irregular (sleep/wake)

(2) High Activity (wake/sleep)
(3) Mild Intensity
(4) Negative Mood

(5, 6, 7, 8, 9, 10) From beginning at home would not go to sleep after nursing. Fussed up to two hours, even with patting or rocking while lying down. If held sitting up, he didn't fuss at all. Got about twelve to fourteen hours of sleep a day. Parents clocked him.

(5) High Activity (wake/sleep)
(6) Nonadaptive (sleep habits)
(7) Negative Mood
(8) Mild Intensity
(9) Persistence-Yes
(10) Distractibility-No

(11) Gradually changed to sleeping longer and going to sleep easier. "Seemed as if he learned to sleep." Change became noticeable after six weeks. (12) To sleep at 6:30–7:00 P.M.; slept till 2:00–4:00 A.M. (13) After that feeding slept only a few hours till 6:00 A.M.

(11) Adaptive (sleep habits)

(12) Regular (sleep/wake)

(13) Moderate Activity (wake/sleep)

(14, 15) After this feeding didn't go to sleep for thirty minutes; sometimes stayed up till next feeding at 10:00 A.M. Often catnapped.

(14) Irregular (wake/sleep)
(15) Moderate Activity (wake/sleep)

(16, 17) Then slept till about 1:00 P.M. Often woke up at intervals. After 2:00 P.M. feeding taken outdoors. *(18) Slept if carriage was moving; woke when it stopped.* By this time holding him sitting up after feeding was no longer necessary.

(16) Irregular (wake/sleep)
(17) Moderate Activity (wake/sleep)
(18) Low Threshold (discrimination)

At nine weeks taken to Chicago by plane due to death of grandparent. *(19, 20, 21, 22, 23, 24) Routine disturbed. His sleeping became irregular; cried a great deal and insistently.*

(19) High Activity (wake/sleep)
(20) Irregular (wake/sleep)
(21) Withdrawal (situation)
(22) High Intensity (social)
(23) Negative Mood
(24) Persistence-Yes

(25, 26) Disturbances became greater as

(25) Nonadaptive (place)

they stayed over four days. Many people coming in and out of house. Also had to sleep in a small cradle out there; *(27, 28) cried* with rocking motion of carriage. *(29, 30, 31, 32) Took about three days after return home to get back to usual routine. Cried a lot and sleeping was irregular. Mother picked him up frequently in those three days. (33) After that it was not necessary. (34) Now sleeps from 7:00 P.M. till 1:00–3:00 A.M., then till 6:00 A.M.; (35, 36) then 7:30–8:30 A.M.; sometimes another short nap before 10:00 A.M. feeding.* (37, 38) Sleeps from end of this feeding till 1:00–2:00 P.M. Sometimes has to be awakened for 2:00 P.M. feeding. *(39, 40) Rarely sleeps after that, except if outdoors.*

FEEDING: Breast-fed, self-demand. *(41) No supplementary bottle, except once in Chicago and once on plane. Took it well, (42) but slowly.* Both breasts at each feeding. Takes an hour, including diapering and burping. *(43) Active sucker. (44) Satiation indicated sometimes by falling asleep; other times by stopping sucking.* Doesn't fuss. Since coming home from hospital made sucking movements of mouth between feedings. This was the main reason for using pacifier; couldn't get him to sleep without it. In past week has gone to sleep after every 6:00 P.M. feeding without pacifier; last night also after 2:00 A.M. feeding. Does some thumbsucking.

(45, 46, 47) Vitamin drops started at three weeks. "Delighted." Made sucking movements; took it very well from the beginning.

(26) *Low Threshold (social)*

(27) *High Intensity*
(28) *Negative Mood*
(29) *Irregular (wake/sleep)*
(30) *Nonadaptive (sleep habits)*
(31) *High Intensity*
(32) *Negative Mood*
(33) *Adaptive (sleep habits)*
(34) *Regular (wake/sleep)*
(35) *Regular with Variable (wake/sleep)*
(36) *Regular (hunger)*
(37) *Regular with Variable (wake/sleep)*
(38) *Regular (hunger)*
(39) *Variable Regular (wake/sleep)*
(40) *Moderate Activity (wake/sleep)*

(41) *Adaptive (food)*

(42) *Low Activity (eating)*

(43) *High Activity (eating)*
(44) *Mild Intensity (satiation)*

(45) *Approach (new food)*
(46) *Mild Intensity (new food)*
(47) *Positive Mood*

(48, 49, 50, 51, 52) Orange juice started yesterday. Diluted in water in bottle. Had been taking water from bottle. Spit out nipple, made face, and cried. Tried it twice. Same reaction. Offered hour later; refused to take nipple in mouth.

(48) *Withdrawal (new food)*
(49) *High Intensity (new food)*
(50) *Negative Mood*
(51) *Persistence-Yes*
(52) *Low Threshold (food)*

(53, 54) Given undiluted orange juice in spoon; took it, tasted it thoroughly in mouth, frowned, then swallowed it and took more. Pabulum at three weeks.

(53) *Approach (new food)*
(54) *Mild Intensity (new food)*

(55, 56) Same first reaction as with orange juice in spoon. Amount increased rapidly to three tablespoons.

(55) *Approach (new food)*
(56) *Mild Intensity (new food)*

(57, 58, 59, 60) At first took it before breast-feeding; after four days had to give him ten to twenty minutes on breast first. Rejected pabulum if offered first, "looks unhappy and screams" after it is put in his mouth.

(57) *Nonadaptive (food)*
(58) *Low Threshold (discrimination)*
(59) *High Intensity (new food)*
(60) *Negative Mood*

(61) Takes it well after the ten minutes on the breast.

(61) *Adaptive (food)*

Bananas and Applesauce started at seven weeks.

(62, 63, 64) Took them well from beginning; screwed up face first time. Always this reaction.

(62) *Approach (new food)*
(63) *Mild Intensity (new food)*
(64) *Negative Mood*

(65, 66) Now smacks lips.

(65) *Adaptive (food)*
(66) *Positive Mood*

Peaches and Pears (67, 68, 69) received same initial response, but did not go to positive response. Also fussed a little.

(67) *Approach (new food)*
(68) *Mild Intensity (new food)*
(69) *Mild Intensity*

(70) Finally stopped because he vomited with them.

(70) *Nonadaptive (food)*

Carrots (71, 72) received same first response yesterday. Refused second spoonful first time. Closed mouth and shook head. (73) Today, mixed with pabulum; took it well.

(71) *Withdrawal (new food)*
(72) *Mild Intensity (new food)*
(73) *High Threshold (food)*

SOILING: *(74) No reaction to being wet. (75, 76, 77, 78) With bowel movement cries most of time. Continues to cry*

(74) *High Threshold (wet)*
(75) *Low Threshold (soiled)*
(76) *High Intensity*

till changed. Mother not sure if this is because he is changed on back which he doesn't like.

(79) One to two bowel movements a day; regular, usually in morning.

BATHING: First time at two weeks. *(80, 81, 82)* "Hated it; screamed."

(83, 84, 85) Continued till tenth week; cried and screamed through entire bath, dressing, and powdering.

(86) At ten weeks "suddenly shut up one day." Silent since then. No actual positive response.

CUTTING NAILS: *(87, 88) If after feeding, no objection. Tried once at other time; kept moving hand, didn't cry.*

MOTILITY: *(89) Very active. Moves all over crib from second week.* Doesn't move much in sleep. Always sleeps on stomach. If on back, plays; does not fall asleep.

SOCIAL: *(90, 91, 92, 93) Never cried at strangers.* "Stares at them and frowns at worst; at best he smiles and talks to them right away."
(94) Responds to strangers smiling or playing with them by smile.

SENSORY: *(95) Jumps at loud noises; doesn't cry.*
(96, 97) Shuts eyes at bright light (sunlight); sometimes cries.
(98, 99, 100, 101) If sung to, will stop his crying. If not crying, smiles at singing.

(77) *Negative Mood*
(78) *Persistence-Yes*

(79) *Regular with Variable (bowel movement)*

(80) *Withdrawal (situation)*
(81) *High Intensity (bath)*
(82) *Negative Mood*
(83) *Nonadaptive (procedures)*
(84) *High Intensity (bath)*
(85) *Negative Mood*
(86) *Adaptive (procedures)*

(87) *Adaptive (procedures)*
(88) *Moderate Activity (motility)*

(89) *High Activity (motility)*

(90) *Approach (new people)*
(91) *Low Threshold (social)*
(92) *Mild Intensity (social)*
(93) *Positive Mood*

(94) *Positive Mood*

(95) *Low Threshold (auditory)*
(96) *Low Threshold (visual)*
(97) *Mood (variable)*
(98) *Low Threshold (auditory)*
(99) *Positive Mood*
(100) *Mild Intensity (auditory)*
(101) *Distractibility-Yes*

(102) In past week "howls back, sounds like little doggie."

(102) High Intensity (social)

B. *Child Two, boy, age one year*

SLEEP: (1) *Put to bed now at 6:00* P.M. *Had been put to bed previously at 7:30–8:00* P.M. Kept up until father came home. *Often got sleepy earlier (5:00– 6:00* P.M.). *Would sleep a bit, then woke up* and put to bed later at 7:30 P.M. About two months ago parents decided it would be better to put him to bed earlier, 6:00 P.M., because he seemed to get tired.

(1) Irregular (sleep/wake)

(2, 3, 4, 5) *First night of the change he cried for twenty minutes; parents didn't go in. The second night he cried for fifteen minutes.*

(2) Nonadaptive (sleep habits)
(3) High Intensity
(4) Negative Mood
(5) Persistence-Yes

(6) *By the fourth night he went right to sleep.* (7, 8, 9) *Since then he goes right to sleep, fusses a minute or two at the most.* In general, less fussing with this early bedtime than with previous later bedtime. (10) *Usually sleeps through night.*

(6) Adaptive (sleep habits)
(7) Regular (sleep/wake)
(8) Mild Intensity
(9) Negative Mood

(10) Low Activity (wake/ sleep)

(11, 12) *For three-day period, bumpers were off crib. During those nights woke up crying at least once.* (13) *In retrospect, parents remember that in Provincetown there were no bumpers on crib and he cried. Once bumpers were replaced, he was all right again.* (14, 15, 16) *Up at 7:15–7:30* A.M. *Plays by himself till picked up fifteen to thirty minutes later. Moves around crib a lot while playing.* (17) *Naps had been irregular.* (18) *Napped in living room with lots of noise around.*

(11) High Intensity
(12) Negative Mood
(13) Low Threshold (discrimination)

(14) Regular (sleep/wake)
(15) Attention Span-Yes
(16) High Activity (motility)

(17) Irregular (wake/sleep)
(18) High Threshold (auditory)

(19, 20, 21, 22, 23) *About six weeks ago, after success with change in evening bedtime, put to bed for morning nap in own room with door closed. Same progression:*

(19) Nonadaptive (sleep habits)
(20) High Intensity
(21) Negative Mood

cried twenty minutes first day, less next day, none after few days.
(24) Duration of morning nap irregular.
(25) Afternoon nap irregular in amount and timing.

(22) Persistence-Yes
(23) Adaptive (sleep habits)
(24) Irregular (wake/sleep)
(25) Irregular (wake/sleep)

FEEDING: Eats well. (26, 27) If satisfied, refuses by pushing food away, spitting, or fussing.
(28) Occasionally plays moderately with the food; tries to get food out of jar with own spoon; tries to feed dog; smears food around. (29) Doesn't distract him from eating. (30, 31) "A real ham, looks at you and giggles."
(32) He had eaten regular food from tray, (33) though he still prefers strained to chopped baby foods.
(34) No fixed food dislikes.
(35) Some days he may refuse food he usually takes well. "Think it has a lot to do with his mood." (36) "Loves the bottle. (37) Cup offered occasionally. Drinks from it willingly (38), but plays around with it, pours it over his head."

(26) Variable Intensity (satiation)
(27) Negative Mood
(28) Moderate Activity (motility)

(29) Distractible-No
(30) Mild Intensity
(31) Positive Mood
(32) Adaptive (food)
(33) Medium Threshold (food)
(34) Adaptive (food)
(35) Variable-Adaptive (food)
(36) Positive Mood
(37) Adaptive (trainability)
(38) Moderate Activity (motility)

BATH: (39, 40, 41, 42) "Absolutely mad about it. Splashes, drinks the water, slides, turns over, bangs his head, comes up laughing. Just great fun."

(39) High Activity (motility)
(40) Adaptive (procedures)
(41) High Intensity
(42) Positive Mood

DRESSING AND UNDRESSING: (43, 44, 45, 46, 47) "Hates it. You have to distract him. Turns and twists, squirms, throws things, sometimes cries. Less objection to being dressed to go out."

(43) High Activity (motility)
(44) Nonadaptive (procedures)
(45) High Intensity
(46) Negative Mood
(47) Distractible-Yes

NAILCUTTING: (48) "Watches; he's fascinated. When younger, used to resist."

(48) Adaptive (procedures)

HAIRCUTTING AND NOSE CLEANING: (49, 50) "Squirms and turns; covers ears; does not cry."

(49) High Activity (motility)
(50) Nonadaptive (procedures)

SOILING: *(51) No reaction to being wet; (52, 53) very occasionally very mild fussing with bowel movement.*
(54) Usually two bowel movements a day; usually early morning and after breakfast.

(51) High Threshold (wet)
(52) Mild Intensity
(53) Negative Mood
(54) Regular (bowel movement)

MOTILITY: *(55) Fairly active during sleep.*
(56) Very active in daytime. He's everywhere. (57, 58) Will stay in playpen if distracted. If parent is in view, will stay in up to forty-five minutes.
(59) Otherwise cries to be taken out.
(60) Can be absorbed by himself with toy for thirty minutes. Walks holding on a great deal. Has not tried walking unsupported.

(55) Moderate Activity (motility)
(56) High Activity (motility)
(57) Adaptive-Variable (places)
(58) Distractible-Yes
(59) Negative Mood
(60) Attention Span-Yes

SOCIAL: *(61, 62, 63) Friendly with strangers. Smiles, responds to their overtures; does not initiate them.*
(64) In stroller outside house, sits very quietly with very little movement and responds very little to people. "He's a different person indoors."
Parallel play with other children his own age; not much direct interaction.
No negative reaction to any person recently. *(65) With some strangers he has seemed to draw back a little in recent weeks.* More overt and intensive responses to parents.
(66, 67, 68, 69) If frustrated or activity stopped, he gets "very mad." Cries very loudly and struggles, but easily distracted. Picks up games with parents or sister very quickly, such as peekaboo.
(70, 71) Laughs loudly. "He's a ham."

(72, 73) "If he's doing something new, he looks at you smiling, expects you to laugh. We usually do; he keeps on smiling."

(61) Approach (new people)
(62) Mild Intensity (social)
(63) Positive Mood
(64) Low Activity (motility)

(65) Moderate Threshold (discrimination)

(66) High Activity (motility)
(67) High Intensity (attempts to control)
(68) Negative Mood
(69) Distractible-Yes
(70) High Intensity
(71) Positive Mood
(72) Mild Intensity (social)
(73) Positive Mood

SENSORY: *(74) Startle reaction now minimal.*

(75) Still turns head and shuts eyes at bright light. Does not cry.

INJECTIONS: *(76, 77, 78) Cried for just a moment when given two polio injections.*

(79, 80) Delighted with pediatrician's office; (81) plays actively with various toys there.

(74) Moderate Threshold (auditory)

(75) Low Threshold (visual)

(76) Moderate Threshold (plain)
(77) Mild Intensity (sensory)
(78) Negative Mood
(79) Adaptive (place)
(80) Positive Mood
(81) High Activity (play)

C. *Child Three, boy, age two years*

SLEEP: *(1) Up to two weeks ago, O.K. Went to sleep and took a nap easily and without fussing. (2) "We never saw him after 6:00 P.M." Always went to sleep at 6:00 P.M. (3) Slept through night.* Mother not sure when he awakened, didn't call till 7:30–8:00 A.M. *(4) Two weeks ago learned to climb out of crib. Climbs out every night and nap time. (5) "He comes in pleased as punch with himself." (6) "If put back in climbs out again." (7, 8) "Can be in and out forty times in an hour." (9) Doesn't fuss, gets right out again.* "I fuss, I yell, I hit him, doesn't do any good." Finally falls asleep. Responds much more quickly when father does it rather than mother. This is true of all disciplining situations, "though I couldn't be firmer."

(1) Adaptive (sleep habits)

(2) Regular (sleep/wake)

(3) Low Activity (sleep/ wake)
(4) High Activity (motility)

(5) Positive Mood
(6) Nonadaptive (sleep habits)
(7) Irregular (sleep/wake)
(8) High Activity (motility)
(9) Persistence-Yes

FEEDING: *(10) Eats well and heartily. (11) Eats everything (12) except vegetables.* Feeds himself mainly by using fingers, but also uses spoon. *(13) Lets mother feed him. (14) Uses glass very well, no bottle at all.* "Gave up bottle same way he gave up strained food. One day he just threw it away." Sucks thumb only when going to sleep.

(10) High Activity (food)
(11) Adaptive (food)
(12) Nonadaptive (food)
(13) Adaptive (procedures)
(14) Adaptive (procedures)

MOTILITY: *(15) Very active, always in motion. (16) Very dexterous in climbing.* "Very safe and cautious." *(17, 18) Approaches new activities, such as using rocking horse, slowly and cautiously first few times. Very rarely falls. (19) If put on bathinette, lies quietly. (20) If put on floor, turns and somersaults immediately.*

(15) High Activity (motility)
(16) High Activity (motility)
(17) Approach (toys)
(18) Low Activity (play)

(19) Low Activity (motility)
(20) High Activity (motility)

BATH: *(21) Plays actively in it.*
(22, 23) "Don't attempt to take him out; he just climbs back." Mother lets water out and takes him out.
(24, 25) Doesn't cry, but may come back later when dressed and climb back into empty tub.

(21) High Activity (motility)
(22) Nonadaptive
     (procedures)
(23) Persistence-Yes

(24) High Activity (motility)
(25) Persistence-Yes

(26, 27, 28) Taken to neighborhood wading pool this summer. Wouldn't go in. Stood at edge for first five to six times. (29, 30) Suddenly went in and enjoyed himself. Said he liked it.
(31, 32) Taken to seashore. Positive reaction from first.
(33) Didn't want to come out, but didn't cry on removal. "He rarely cries, he accepts his fate."

(26) Withdrawal (place)
(27) Low Activity (motility)
(28) Nonadaptive (place)
(29) Adaptive (place)
(30) Positive Mood
(31) Approach (place)
(32) Positive Mood
(33) Nonadaptive·
     (procedures)

WASHING HAIR AND FACE: *(34, 35, 36)* "Impossible. Screams and squirms."

(34) High Activity (motility)
(35) High Intensity
(36) Negative Mood

NAILCUTTING: *(37)* "Also almost impossible. Squirms, pulls away, doesn't cry."

(37) High Activity (motility)

HAIRCUTS: Cooperative third one (previous history), *(38, 39, 40, 41) then began objecting; screamed, tugged at towels around him.*

(38) Moderate Activity
     (motility)
(39) Nonadaptive
     (procedures)
(40) High Intensity
(41) Negative Mood

(42) Haircut without towels around him,

(42) Adaptive (procedures)

was O.K. *(43, 44, 45, 46) During last one screamed, squirmed a lot. Taken out without haircut.* Mother thinks he was tired; also, had towel around him again.

DRESSING: *(47, 48, 49, 50) Very cooperative, smiles, helps with various garments.*

(51, 52) No objection to diapering, lies quietly. Takes shoes and socks off. Tries to dress himself; when unsuccessful doesn't fuss. When he can't put his own shoes on, puts sister's on. *(53, 54) "He's happy with that." Grins a little.*

PLAY: *(55) Sometimes will play by himself from one to two hours. (56) At other times will get involved "in mischief," such as pulling out toys or trying to involve mother. (57) Will play with one toy from fifteen to twenty minutes. (58) With difficult toy is very persistent, doesn't show frustration.* Sometimes asks for help. *(59, 60) When successful he has very positive reaction, "very excited and proud of himself.* Comes and asks for my approval." *(61) Takes to new toys quickly. (62, 63) Plays very well with sister,* laughs and shouts with her. She is much more tolerant of him than several months ago. Imitates everything she does. In past six weeks he has begun to play with other children his own age. *(64) Pushed by another child, pushed back.* "Very unaggressive child." *(65) Allows others to grab toys away without grabbing back or crying. If holding toy firmly and it is grabbed, sometimes will hold on tightly.*

SOILING: *(66, 67) No fussing when wet or soiled.* Sometimes makes game of

(43) Nonadaptive (procedures)
(44) High Activity (motility)
(45) High Intensity
(46) Negative Mood
(47) Moderate Activity (motility)
(48) Adaptive (procedures)
(49) Mild Intensity (dress)
(50) Positive Mood
(51) Low Activity (motility)
(52) Adaptive (procedures)

(53) Mild Intensity
(54) Positive Mood

(55) Attention Span-Yes
(56) Attention Span-Variable

(57) Attention Span-Yes

(58) Persistence-Yes

(59) Positive Mood
(60) High Intensity

(61) Approach (toys)
(62) Positive Mood
(63) High Intensity

(64) High Activity (motility)
(65) Persistence-No and Variable

(66) High Threshold (wet)
(67) High Threshold

calling mother to change his diaper. *(68, 69, 70) Will sit on toilet cheerfully, but only for few minutes, and then hops off.*
(71) Has not made bowel movement on toilet seat.

SOCIAL: *(72, 73) Quick positive responses to strangers; if men, often takes initiative. (74) With women, takes long time to warm up.*
(75, 76, 77) If mother leaves house, cries; stops quickly after she has left.

DISCIPLINE: *(78, 79, 80) "If he feels like doing something that is forbidden, he does it. Looks at you and laughs."*

(81) Can't distract him with toy or game. (82, 83) "Cannot teach him not to run into street."

(84) If he starts to run into street and parent or sister calls him, pays no attention. No results from spanking: "So many things I spank him for." *(85) Usually ignores the spank, sometimes cries briefly.*

SENSORY: *(86) Does not cry if he falls and hurts himself. (87) Also, when he has a cold and stuffed nose, fusses very little.*

SPEECH: No real advance, has ten or twelve words. Won't repeat words on mother's request.

(soiled)
(68) Adaptive (procedures)
(69) Mild Intensity
(70) Positive Mood

(71) Nonadaptive (trainability)

(72) Approach (new people)
(73) Positive Mood
(74) Withdrawal (new people)

(75) High Intensity
(76) Negative Mood
(77) Persistence-No

(78) Nonadaptive (trainability)
(79) Mild Intensity (social)
(80) Positive Mood
(81) Distractible-No
(82) Nonadaptive (trainability)
(83) Persistence-Yes

(84) Distractible-No

(85) Variable Mood

(86) High Threshold (pain)
(87) High Threshold (discomfort)

TABLE 14

CATEGORY SCORES FOR THE THREE PROTOCOLS PRESENTED IN APPENDIX II.

CHILD (Age in Mos.)	Total	Activity			Rhythmicity			Adaptability			Approach			Threshold			Intensity			Mood			Distractibility			Persistence		
		H	M	L	R	V	I	A	V	N	A	V	W	H	M	L	I	V	M	+V		−	Y	V	N	Y	V	N
Child One 3 mos.	104*	5	5	1	7	4	5	7	0	6	6	0	4	2	0	8	9	0	12	5	1	11	1	0	1	4	0	0
Child Two 12 mos.	81	7	3	2	3	0	4	8	2	4	1	0	0	2	4	2	7	1	6	7	0	10	3	0	1	4	0	0
Child Three 24 mos.	88**	12	2	5	1	0	1	9	0	10	4	0	2	4	0	0	6	0	4	10	1	3	0	0	2	7	2	3

* Items 35 and 37 scored for both regular and variable, giving two additional items in total scoring.

** Item 65 scored in persistence category for both no and variable, giving one additional item in total scoring.

Index